Our Moral Life in Christ

Student Workbook

Zach Bairo (signature)

featuring

Dear Mark & Maddie

The Didache Series

Our Moral Life in Christ

Student Workbook

featuring

Dear Mark & Maddie

Midwest Theological Forum
Woodridge, Illinois

Published in the United States of America by

Midwest Theological Forum
1420 Davey Road
Woodridge, IL 60517

Author: Rev. Fred Gatschet

General Editor: Rev. James Socias

Associate Editors: Kimberly D. Chojnicki, Stephen J. Chojnicki, Randal Powers

Editorial Board: Rev. James Socias, Rev. Peter Armenio, Kimberly Kirk Hahn,
        Dr. Scott Hahn, Mike Aquilina

Layout Design: Kimberly D. Chojnicki

Disclaimer: The editor of this book has attempted to give proper credit to all sources used in the text and illustrations. Any miscredit or lack of credit is unintended and will be corrected in the next edition.

ISBN 978-1-890177-61-4

Printed in Canada

Contents

To the Student:

Christian morality is the area of study where all the other religious disciplines come into focus. In the *Didache Series*, you have been given an introduction to Catholicism, an explanation of the Bible, and a tour through the history of the Church. Morality is where we learn to apply everything. There is not much point in learning the Ten Commandments or the Beatitudes, for example, if we do not put them into practice.

As a religion teacher in a Catholic high school, I have come to appreciate the questions that young people have. They are searching for answers in a world that has by and large abandoned them to the television and popular culture to try to figure out what is right and wrong. Sadly, some people go down this road. Many others, however, are looking for something more substantial. It is my experience with these questions, conflicts, fears, and uncertainties of my own students that led me to write *Dear Mark and Maddie*. In fact, one of my students, whose name is Maddie, immediately recognized herself in the letters that begin each chapter as I was teaching her class out of the prototype of this workbook!

Our Moral Life in Christ does a masterful job of setting the cornerstone for Christian morality: the love of God. If we do not love God, living as he has taught us through his Son makes absolutely no sense. Hopefully, as you work through this study, who will grow to appreciate just how much the Father loves you. Learning to deepen your love for him in return, you will naturally desire all the more to know how he wants you to live, and then willingly adopt the Christian lifestyle with love.

I have tried to make the examples in this workbook as concrete as possible to illustrate the points being made in the text. Some may wonder if Christian morality really has to be this complicated. It would seem so, based on two observations. The first is that human life is complicated. The second is the fact that people like St. Paul had to write lengthy letters to explain the subtle nuances of the Christian life. This would suggest that the Christian life has always been a little complex. But the Catholic Church teaches that anyone who takes the trouble to study can know with certainty the answers to life's complicated and difficult questions. The desire of myself and your teachers would be that, after studying the text and working the exercises in this workbook, you will come to know and understand better the plan that God has for you, and that his plan is the only way to true freedom in this life, and eternal joy in the life that is to come.

God's blessings to you,

Fr. Fred Gatschet
Author, *Our Moral Life in Christ Workbook*

Name _____

Date _____

Hour _____

Chapter 1: Preliminary Notions

Dear Mark and Maddie —

I always thought of myself as a good Catholic. I mean, like my family and I always go to Mass on Sunday, and we celebrate things like Christmas and Easter at home. I'm not saying I'm perfect or anything, but when I'm with my boyfriend and out with my friends, I stay away from most of what some of the other people in my class are doing . . . you know what I mean. But lately I have been wondering why. My brother went away to college last year, and he says that we need to be more open-minded. He says that nobody really knows the truth. He learned that right and wrong depend on the feelings and experience of the individual, and that religion makes people puppets instead of independent thinkers. At least that's what they told him in college. What if he's right? How do I know all this Christianity stuff is true? Sure, I have seen a lot of my friends get into a lot of trouble with alcohol and sex. Many of them spend most of the little time they are at home arguing with their parents. I guess it's no wonder they want to escape to the parties all the time. I want to do the right thing, but it seems I'm missing out on a lot of fun, too. How do I know what is true?

— A Wondering and Wandering Senior

After reading the chapter, write a response to this letter:

Dear W & W:

SOME PRELIMINARY NOTIONS

1. On page 2 of the text, the question is posed that if asked, many people could not recite the Ten Commandments in order, and many people would not know the Eight Beatitudes. In your freshman year, when you studied *Introduction to Catholicism* a better part of that textbook was dedicated to explaining the Decalogue and the Beatitudes. Do you remember them? Write them in the space provided on the next page. If you have forgotten them, you will find the Ten Commandments in Exodus 20: 1-17 and Deuteronomy 5: 6-21. The versions of the Ten Commandments from Exodus and Deuteronomy, along with the Traditional Catechetical Form, may be found in *The Catechism of the Catholic Church* immediately preceding paragraph 2052. The Beatitudes may be found in the Gospel of St. Matthew 5: 3-12 and in *The Catechism of the Catholic Church*, paragraph 1716.

    The Ten Commandments:

    1.

    2.

    3.

    4.

    5.

    6.

    7.

    8.

    9.

    10.

    The Eight Beatitudes

    1.

    2.

    3.

4.

5.

6.

7.

8.

I. CHRISTIANITY IS NOT MERELY A MORALITY.

2. On page 3 of the text, the word "humanism" is introduced. What does it mean?

3. Find an example of where you have seen humanist thinking in action, or people being guided in their lives by humanist principles, and explain it.

II. CHRISTIANITY INCLUDES A MORALITY.

4. The Cardinal Virtues are listed on page 4. Below are some cases where the virtues might be applied. Write the name of the virtue that would be called upon to resolve each case and write a brief explanation beneath each as to why you think the virtue you wrote applies to the situation.

_____ Mike loves to play video games. The interactive games on the internet are especially attractive to him. He can sit at the computer for hours, sometimes even losing an entire night's sleep playing games, and once in a while he looks at pornographic websites.

_____ Melissa has had ambitious career plans ever since she started high school. She demands a lot out of herself and pushes herself hard. Recently her sister's baby died. During and after the funeral, Melissa has been questioning her values and the real meaning of her life.

_____ Jorge and Carissa have been dating for a few months now. Jorge has been getting more assertive in the physical dimension of the relationship, and Carissa has been equally receptive to Jorge's advances. They have both talked about "not wanting to go too far" but once they get together, neither seems to be able to control him/herself.

_____ Kevin owns a t-shirt printing business. Oftentimes he finds himself having to cut his own pay to make sure his workers are paid their full wages on time.

5. On page 5 of the text, the theological virtues of Faith, Hope, and Charity (Love) are explained. They originate in the Bible in 1 Corinthians 13: 13 and 1 Thessalonians 1: 3. The text states that the theological virtues "inform the cardinal virtues and give life to them." What does this mean? For example . . .

   a. How would the theological virtue of Faith inform and give life to the cardinal virtue of Fortitude in the case of Jorge and Carissa in Question #4?

    b. How would the theological virtue of Hope inform and give life to the cardinal virtue of Prudence in the case of Melissa?

    c. How would the theological virtue of Charity (Love) inform and give life to the cardinal virtue of Justice in the case of Kevin and his t-shirt business?

III. CHRISTIANITY IS A RELIGIOUS MORALITY.

A. THE CONCEPTS OF GOOD AND EVIL ARE DETERMINED BY GOD.

6. This is a true story. A bishop was visiting a class of candidates for Confirmation. In his discussion with the group, he asked them how precisely we know what is good and what is evil; what makes something good or evil? According to the text, what is the answer to this question?

7. After the bishop explained what you just wrote above, one young man countered with the statement, "Well, I suppose God is entitled to his opinion, but I am also entitled to mine!" Comment on this young man's response. (Hint: Is God even capable of having an opinion?)

8. What is the cause of the flawed nature that we inherit from Adam and Eve?

9. The text cites a key piece of St. Paul's writing from the Letter to the Romans. More of what comes before and what follows that verse (Romans 7: 14-25) is provided here.

"¹⁴We know that the law is spiritual, but I am carnal, sold under sin. ¹⁵I do not understand my own actions. For I do not do what I want, but I do the very thing I hate. ¹⁶Now if I do what I do not want, I agree that the law is good. ¹⁷So then, it is no longer I that do it, but sin which dwells within me. ¹⁸For I know that nothing good dwells within me, that is, in my flesh. I can will what is right, but I cannot do it. ¹⁹For I do not do the good I want, but the evil I do not want is what I do. ²⁰Now if I do what I do not want, it is no longer I that do it, but sin which dwells within me. ²¹So I find it to be a law that when I want to do right, evil lies close at hand. ²²For I delight in the law of God, in my inmost self, ²³but I see in my members another law at war with the law of my mind, and making me captive to the law of sin which dwells in my members. ²⁴Wreched man that I am! Who will deliver me from this body of death? ²⁵Thanks be to God through Jesus Christ our Lord! So then, I of myself serve the law of God with my mind, but with my flesh, I serve the law of sin."

    a. St. Paul is one of the architects of Christianity. Yet, does he claim to have mastered sin in his own life? How does he describe his own moral struggles?

    b. How does this take away from, or add to St. Paul's moral authority? That is, given this self-confessed state of St. Paul's own life, does he have any business telling other people how to live theirs?

How St. Paul resolves this conflict (vv. 24-25 & 1 Corinthians 15: 10) leads us to the next section. . . .

B. THE ETHICAL REQUIREMENTS OF THE GOSPEL REQUIRE THE AID OF GOD'S GRACE.

10. When do we receive sanctifying grace?

Zach Baixo

11. Some flawed and erroneous teachings on grace claim that grace covers over what is displeasing to God, so that when God looks upon sinful humanity, he sees his grace instead of our sins. How is this false?

12. When do we receive actual grace?

13. While we need grace to conform ourselves to God's will, there are certain aspects of obeying God that come more naturally than others. What would some of these be?

14. On the other hand, as the heading of this section states, the ethical requirements of the Gospel require the aid of God's grace. The text lists some of these requirements. Also, read Luke 6: 27-36. What are some of the ethical requirements of the Gospel that do not come naturally, that we will need God's grace to fulfill?

IV. CHRISTIAN MORALITY IS A MORALITY OF FOLLOWING AND IMITATING CHRIST.

15. Review the five elements that comprise the morality of following and imitating Jesus on page 8 of the text. Then review the letter from "Wondering and Wandering Senior" and apply the five elements to her questions and situation.

The Call or Vocation — *How has this young lady been called by God?*

The Response — *How has she already responded to God? What more does she need to do?*

The Following — *Christian morality consists in striving to live as Jesus did. How is she doing so, and what more should she be striving for?*

Discipleship — *Read how the book defines discipleship. How does one become a disciple of Jesus?*

The Imitation — *How would being a Christian be like training to be a good athlete or musician?*

V. IDENTIFICATION WITH CHRIST: NEW LIFE IN THE HOLY SPIRIT

16. We live in a time where individual freedom and choice are championed as the highest values by which people ought to live. Yet, as this section of the text explains, St. Paul refers many times to "putting on Christ" and essentially to abandoning his own life in favor of living the way Jesus did (*"... it is no longer I who live, but Christ who lives in me; and the life I now live in the flesh I live by faith in the Son of God, who loved me and give himself for me."* Galatians 2: 20). Explain how these two ways of life conflict with one another.

17. There are many examples of people who simply abandon Christ to live lives of disorder and mortal sin. These are easy to identify. What is more common are those of us trying to have it both ways. That is, name an example or two of where either you yourself, or others you have seen, claim to follow Jesus, but still cling to their own ways. (For a help, refer to Galatians 5: 19-21. St. Paul lists a number of sins and warns that those who do these things will not inherit the kingdom of God. Do you see others committing these sins and then going to Communion on Sunday? Do you?)

VI. CHARACTERISTICS OF CHRISTIAN MORALITY

A. CHRISTIAN MORALITY FIRST AFFECTS THE *PERSON* AND THEN THE *ACTION*.

18. Another true story: A couple presented themselves to the parish priest, desiring to baptize their newborn baby. In the course of their conversation with the priest, it came out that the couple was not married and did not attend Mass on Sunday. In the course of discussing this "irregularity" the mother asked if the Baptism could take place on a Thursday. The priest informed her that since Baptism is a participation in the Resurrection of Jesus, they are usually done on Sunday, the day of the Resurrection, unless there is a serious reason to have the Baptism on another day. When asked her reason for wanting the Baptism on Thursday, she informed the priest it was because the godfather they had selected had to report to jail on Friday for a domestic violence conviction. When the priest inquired as to who the victim was, he was told it was the live-in girlfriend of the prospective godfather, who was also to be the godmother.

    Your text states on page 11, *"Therefore, the Beatitudes, which express the heart of Christian morality, speak to the inner attitude of the person. The Christian must first accept the idea of being merciful, pure of heart, a peacemaker, and then the actions will follow."* With this in mind, if you had been the priest in the case mentioned above, what would you have told the couple?

B. CHRISTIAN MORALITY TRANSFORMS FIRST THE SOUL AND THEN THE MORAL APPEARANCE.

19. After reading this section, answer the following:

    "Somebody in the privacy of their own home, looking at pornography is not hurting anyone. What goes on in the confines of one's home is nobody else's business."

    "Society is just being hypocritical by not allowing marijuana for personal use. They allow alcohol, and that causes enough damage. People don't get violent when they get high on pot like they do when they're drunk. I may be breaking the law when I smoke weed, but at least I'm not a hypocrite. And besides, those laws are stupid."

C. CHRISTIAN MORALITY ENCOMPASSES THE ATTITUDES OF THE PERSON.

20. In what two ways does frequent reception of the Sacrament of Penance help us to habitually make good moral decisions?

    a.

    b.

21. This section describes a cycle. Fill in the the missing components.

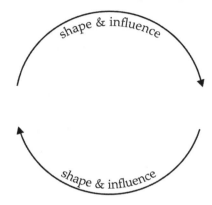

D. CHRISTIAN MORALITY ACCOUNTS FOR WHAT IS FORBIDDEN, BUT STRESSES MORE WHAT OUGHT TO BE DONE.

Positive and Negative Morality

Following are the first four amendments to the Constitution of the United States. Read them.

Amendment 1
> Congress shall make no law respecting an establishment of religion, or prohibiting the free exercise thereof; or abridging the freedom of speech, or of the press; or of the right of the people peaceably to assemble, and to petition the Government for a redress of grievances.

Amendment 2
> A well regulated Militia, being necessary to the security of a free State, the right of the people to keep and bear arms shall not be infringed.

Amendment 3
> No Soldier shall in time of peace be quartered in any house without the consent of the Owner, or in time of war, but in a manner to be prescribed by law.

Amendment 4
> The right of the people to be secure in their persons, houses, papers, and effects, against unreasonable searches and seizures, shall not be violated, and no Warrants shall issue, but upon probable cause, supported by Oath or affirmation, and particularly describing the place to be searched, and the persons or things to be seized.

22. These form the basis of some of our basic civil liberties as Americans. They are essentially the contract between us and the Federal Government. What do you notice about them? That is, in general, what does the Government have to do to fulfill its end of the contract?

23. What about most of the Ten Commandments?
    1. I am the Lord your God, you shall not have strange gods before me.
    2. You shall not take the name of the Lord your God in vain.
    3. Remember to keep holy the Lord's day.
    4. Honor your father and your mother.
    5. You shall not kill.
    6. You shall not commit adultery.
    7. You shall not steal.
    8. You shall not bear false witness against your neighbor.
    9. You shall not covet your neighbor's wife.
    10. You shall not covet your neighbor's goods.

    With the exception of the Third and Fourth Commandments, what kind of morality is exemplified by the rest?

24. Now, what about the Beatitudes? Explain what kind of law they are.

25. What would be the relationship between positive and negative law? Is one better than the other? Should one be placed above another?

26. Which kind of law does Jesus most emphasize in his teachings?

27. Which kinds of sins does Jesus think are most serious?

38. In some intellectual circles, people of faith are routinely maligned for placing their hope in God. Some who consider themselves to be quite intelligent make the accusation that if God is so loving and just, why does he allow for people to be poor, and oppressed? Why does he allow wars to take place?

E. CHRISTIAN MORALITY REQUIRES NOT ONLY JUST ACTIONS, BUT ALSO HOLINESS.

29. "Those Christians are all such hypocrites. Sure they go to church on Sunday and say prayers, but I know lots of people who, instead of wasting their time in church, help the community by volunteering for Big Brothers and Big Sisters, or delivering Meals on Wheels." How would you answer this? (Hint: Mother Teresa insisted that the sisters in her order spend a certain amount of time each day in prayer, as she herself did. Was this a waste of time that could have been better spent seeing to the needs of the poor and dying of Calcutta?)

30. How are acts of Christian charity and a life of holiness related to one another?

F. CHRISTIAN MORALITY IS NOT A RIGID MORALITY MARKED BY A MULTIPLICITY OF PRECEPTS.

31. The claim that Christian morality (especially as described by Catholic teaching) is not about a bunch of rules would strike many people as strange if not downright untrue. How would you explain this?

G. THE MORALITY PREACHED BY JESUS IS A MORALITY
THAT INCLUDES BOTH REWARD AND PUNISHMENT.

32. There are two erroneous teachings in our society that this section will correct. The first is the statement that is often made that since God is so loving and merciful, he simply cannot consign any of his children to hell. The second comes from a number of evangelical protestant denominations claiming that once a person "gets saved" by "accepting Jesus Christ as his/her personal Lord and Savior" that that person's salvation is assured. Read the following citations from the Bible and comment on these statements.

Matthew 16: 27

Matthew 25: 31-46

Romans 2: 4-11

2 Corinthians 5: 10

Philippians 2: 12

Revelation 14: 13

Revelation 22: 12

H. CHRISTIAN MORALITY IS MORALITY FOR FREEDOM.

33. How is the Christian understanding of freedom different from how our society understands it?

34. The claim that God's laws enhance our freedom sounds strange to many people. How can laws make us free? Don't laws restrict what we can do? Yet, imagine if for some mysterious reason, everyone without exception strictly obeyed the Seventh Commandment 100% of the time. Would we have more or less freedom? How would the loss of the "freedom to steal" affect all of us?

35. Every year, numbers and statistics are compiled as to how much, for example, cigarette smoking and obesity cost the economy in terms of health-care dollars spent and lost productivity. How much do you think we waste every year as a society by disobeying the Ten Commandments? List three concrete examples of how money and other resources are wasted by misusing our freedom.

    a.

    b.

    c.

I. CHRISTIAN MORALITY IS FULFILLED ON EARTH,
BUT IT PERTAINS TO THE NEXT LIFE.

36. Which two extremes does Christian morality seek to avoid?

    a.

    b.

37. How ought the Christian to understand these two? How do they fit together?

J. CHRISTIAN MORALITY FINDS ITS BEGINNING AND END IN LOVE.

38. The Greek language in which the New Testament is written has a number of words for "love." One is *eros* which describes the love of physical attraction. The second one, *philia*, is the love of feelings and emotions. The last one, *agape*, is the love that sacrifices its own wants and needs for the good of someone else. Which one is described in this section? How do you know?

K. THE CHRISTIAN MORAL LIFE FINDS ITS NOURISHMENT IN MASS AND THE SACRAMENTS.

39. The citation on page 17 from the *General Catechetical Directory* states: "The Church ardently desires that all the Christian faithful be brought into that full, conscious and active participation which is required by the very nature of the liturgy and the dignity of the baptismal priesthood." When it says that full, conscious, and active participation is required by the very nature of the liturgy those attending Mass, it means that without such participation, the celebration comes up short. Sadly, oftentimes at Mass, many people (young and old) simply go through the motions, and participation is anything but full, conscious, and active. Based on the title of this section, what do you think might be the connection between lax participation at Mass, and an adulterous affair that ruins a marriage; or many of the problems that plague the young, such as drug and alcohol abuse, sexual misconduct, not finishing high school, etc.?

MARK AND MADDIE RESPOND

Dear W & W —

Wow! What a letter! We are glad to see that you practice your faith with your family, and hope you keep it up. The very fact that you are asking such questions is, we think, God Himself prodding you to get to know Him better. Christianity is not about following a bunch of rules. It is about falling in love with God by getting to know His Son, Jesus Christ. As Catholics we are so blessed. We can get to know Jesus by reading His words and actions in the Gospels. And He invites us into an intimate communion with Him in the Sacrament of the Eucharist. Although there are many beautiful and intellectually stimulating facets of our faith, it all comes down to loving Jesus, and out of love for Him, doing what He has asked us to do if we are to call ourselves His friends. That is why we learn the Commandments and the other demands of our faith—it's kind of hard to follow and obey something if you don't know what it is! To someone who either does not know Jesus or does not want to get to know Him, none of this will make any sense. This is probably what your brother has been exposed to in college.

Keep up the good fight! Jesus is waiting for you, and we are praying for you.

Peace,

Mark & Maddie

Name _____

Date _____

Hour _____

Chapter 3: Freedom and the Moral Act

Dear Mark and Maddie —

My parents and I are always at each other's throat. I am almost eighteen and not a little kid anymore. They just don't want to respect my freedom. I am not a bad kid. I check in with my parents, and always tell them where I am going. If I am going to be late getting home, I always call. But they still won't let me just be on my own. What can I do to get them to loosen up a little and give me more freedom, because until they do, I might as well just be

— Stuck in the Straightjacket

How would you answer "Stuck's" letter? So far, "Stuck" seems to be insisting on freedom, but what is missing from the letter?

INTRODUCTION

1. The text states that freedom, conscience, and law are rational principles of moral life that apply to everyone. Furthermore, the text claims that we can only achieve a worthy human existence by imitating Jesus. Look up the following citations from Scripture and explain how Jesus lived these principles and how we can imitate him.

Rational Principles	Jesus	Us
Freedom which makes us a moral agent (i.e, freedom allows us to act on our own authority and be responsible for our actions)	Luke 4: 1-13	
Conscience that gives us the capacity to discover God's will as written on our souls	Mark 14: 32-42	
Law, which allows freedom to function properly	Luke 2: 51-52	

I. IMPORTANCE OF THE MORAL LIFE

2. *Right moral conduct perfects the human being, and wrong moral conduct degrades him.* How?

   Scenario A: One of Tom's friends has introduced him and his group of friends to the use of marijuana, and how to obtain it easily. Some of Tom's friends have started to smoke it. Others have quit associating with the group. Tom is still in the group. He knows that he should not have anything to do with any illegal drug, but he is still wondering what to do.

   How would Tom's refusal to use the drug perfect him, and make him a better man?

   If he caves in to the temptation and peer pressure, how would he (i.e., his character as a man) be degraded?

Scenario B: Ellie was in a car accident that caused some damage to her car. It was the other driver's fault. She had her car fixed, and the other driver's insurance company paid the bill. About a month later, Ellie received a check in the mail, made out to her, from the other driver's insurance company for $2,316.87, the exact same amount as the body shop had estimated for the repair to her car. She called the body shop, and was informed that they were paid in full. Ellie's mother's boyfriend told her that the insurance company probably just made a mistake. She should just cash the check, and enjoy her windfall. He told her that since insurance companies are used to dealing with billions of dollars, a couple of thousand dollars is not even real money to them.

How would returning the check to the insurance company help to morally perfect Ellie?

How would she be degraded if she cashed the check and spent the money? (Hint: First Century poet and orator Silius Italicus once wrote: *Ipsa quidem virtus sibimet pulcherrima mereces* or *Virtue herself is her own sweetest reward*. How would this apply to Ellie?)

II. MAN'S ABILITY TO CHOOSE GOOD AND EVIL

3. A pack-rat finds a woman's diamond earring and picks it up and takes it to its nest. A man sweeping the floor in a dance hall after a wedding reception finds a woman's diamond earring, pawns it, and pockets the cash. In both cases, it is highly unlikely that the woman will ever see her diamond earring again. Why is the pack-rat's action amoral (i.e., neither good nor evil) while what the man did would be considered an act of theft?

4. The fact that people are morally responsible for their actions makes _____ possible, and therefore _____ is necessary.

5. Over the millennia, a lot of ink has been spilled by thousands of philosophers, theologians, politicians, and the like, over what is right and wrong and how right and wrong are determined. Why does any of this matter to the Christian? What is depending on our knowing what is good and evil, and then deciding for the good and rejecting evil?

III. THE HUMAN ACT, A MORAL ACT

6. Below are some examples of actions that can be done by human beings. Indicate whether moral good or evil can be attributed to each, and tell why.

Act	Can moral good be attributed?	Why?
A young man has a dream full of sexually erotic images.	YES NO	
A man goes into diabetic shock while driving his car, loses consciousness, and causes an accident that kills two people.	YES NO	
A woman has too much to drink and her drunkenness causes an accident that kills two people.	YES NO	
A group of college students spends the evening in a dorm room looking at pornography on the internet.	YES NO	
A young woman gets an abortion because she is frightened, confused, and forced into it by her parents.	YES NO	
A young woman gets an abortion because she does not want to be "inconvenienced" by the pregnancy.	YES NO	

IV. KNOWLEDGE AS A CONDITION FOR MORALITY

A. FULL KNOWLEDGE

7. A married man is out of town on a business meeting. After a long day of presentations and work, he goes to the hotel's lounge for some dinner and to relax. While there, he meets a single woman, and they begin to talk. After a few drinks, and as they are getting to be more familiar, she interjects into the conversation that she is on birth control pills. The man reassures her that pregnancy is not a concern because he had a vasectomy after he and his wife had their second child. The man and woman later retire to his hotel room, where they spend the evening having sex with one another. Later, full of remorse, the man confides in the priest during confession that "one thing just led to another, and I just don't know how this happened!" Comment on this case.

B. PARTIAL KNOWLEDGE

8. A young man migrates to the Unites States illegally. He knows what he is doing is illegal because he sneaks into the country in a shipping container, and leaves the container, once unloaded in New York Harbor, under cover of darkness. He has broken the legitimate law of a sovereign nation that has the right to determine who crosses its borders. Yet the man was driven by poverty, hunger, and the fear of being killed by marauders in his own country where chaos reigns. A restaurant owner immediately hires him, knowing he is in the country illegally, but the owner was not having any luck finding and retaining workers for his business. The owner pays the foreign employee in cash to avoid reporting his income to the Internal Revenue Service and to Social Security.

V. THE FREE HUMAN ACT

9. The text states that the higher the stage of freedom a person reaches, he will be capable of higher levels of morality. In the Gospel of St. Luke 12: 47-48, Jesus tell us in the Parable of the Faithful and Unfaithful Slave: *"And that servant who knew his master's will, but did not make ready or act according to his will, shall receive a severe beating. But he who did not know, and did what deserved a beating, shall receive a light beating. Every one to whom much is given, of him will much be required; and of him to whom men commit much they will demand the more."*

   What is Jesus teaching us about the relationship between moral responsibility and culpability for the way we live our lives?

10. St. Paul uses the image of being a slave to sin, as does the text on page 49. In Romans 6: 20-23, he writes: *"When you were slaves of sin, you were free in regard to righteousness. But then what return did you get from the things of which you now are ashamed? The end of those things is death. But now that you have been freed from sin and and have become slaves of God, the return you get is sanctification and its end, eternal life. For the wages of sin is death, but the free gift of God is eternal life in Christ Jesus our Lord."*

    When St. Paul says that when his readers were slaves to sin, they were free in regards to righteousness, what does he mean?

    How does this same thinking apply to you the student, who is studying this course on Christian Morality?

    Given your answer to the previous question, and St. Paul's exhortation, why should you study Christian Morality?

11. And in Galatians 5: 1, St. Paul writes, *"For freedom Christ has set us free; stand fast therefore, and do not submit again to a yoke of slavery."* What does he mean by this?

A. EXISTENCE OF FREEDOM

12. St. Paul warns the Galatians in 5: 19-21, *"Now the works of the flesh are plain: immorality, impurity, licentiousnes, idolatry, sorcery, enmity, strife, jealousy, anger, selfishness, dissension, party spirit, envy, drunkenness, carousing, and the like. I warn you, as I warned you before, that those who do such things shall not inherit the kingdom of God."* This is a list of sins that St. Paul warns will result in someone losing their soul (i.e., going to hell) if they do not repent of them. What does *licentiousness* mean and how is it opposed to freedom?

B. FREEDOM AND KNOWLEDGE OF THE TRUTH

13. The text states that the intimate relationship between freedom and truth is broken when a person tries to determine what is right and wrong according to his likes and dislikes. How did Adam and Eve fail in this regard? (Review Genesis 3: 6, if you are not sure.)

14. How do people your age fall into the same trap today?

C. FREEDOM AND THE GOOD

15. If freedom means only the ability to choose good, then how can it be freedom? (If you need some help, re-read the example of the student practicing music on p. 45.)

D. FREEDOM AND RESPONSIBILITY

16. Next to Jesus himself, Moses is without a doubt, the greatest liberator in the Bible. The stories contained in the Books of Exodus and Numbers are epic sagas of a people coming to grips with freedom and its demands. As you may remember from *Understanding the Scriptures*, the better part of the Book of Numbers is the story of the Israelite people wandering in the desert. Read the following citations:

"'O that we had meat to eat! We remember the fish we ate in Egypt for nothing, the cucumbers, the melons, the leeks, the onions, and the garlic; but now our strength is dried up, and there is nothing at all but this manna to look at'" (Numbers 11: 4-6).

"Then all the congregation raised a loud cry; and the people wept that night. And all the people of Israel murmured against Moses and Aaron; the whole congregation said to them, 'Would that we had died in the land of Egypt! Or would that we had died in this wilderness! Why does the LORD bring us into this land, to fall by the sword? Our wives and our little ones will become a prey; would it not be better for us to go back to Egypt?' And again they said to one another, 'Let us choose a captain, and go back to Egypt'" (Numbers 14: 1-4).

The Israelites have their freedom. While slaves in Egypt, they called out to God, Who heard them, and sent Moses to free them. Now they are free, but what do they seem to prefer? How are they dealing with the responsibility that goes with their freedom?

How are people today like or not like the ancient Israelites?

Benjamin Franklin once said, "They that can give up essential liberty to obtain a little temporary safety deserve neither liberty nor safety." – *Historical Review of Pennsylvania 1759*

What are Franklin and the Old Testament saying about the relationship between freedom (liberty) and responsibility?

E. GOD'S RESPECT OF HUMAN FREEDOM

17. Many times people will ask, "If God is so powerful, why can't he just make all the evil in the world go away? Why does he allow all this suffering and injustice?" How would you answer that question?

F. FREEDOM AND DIVINE GRACE

18. How would habitually doing good in those daily things that we know well help us to do the right thing in a moment of confusion or personal crisis?

G. FREEDOM AND LAW

19. Imagine that an aspiring young basketball player presents himself to the coach, expressing his burning desire to be the best basketball player in history. The coach is impressed with his enthusiasm and spirit and accepts him on the team. But as the young player begins to attend practices, problems develop. First of all, the new player is not always on time for practice, and sometimes does not show up at all. Then he refuses to accept the boundaries of the court. If he is out of bounds and gets called on it, he gets angry and huffs off ranting, "I wasn't out by much. Why do you people get so uptight if someone is a few inches out of bounds?? What's the big deal?!?"

What is the relationship between the hard and fast rules of basketball and becoming a first-rate player? How do the rules help someone to be a good player or prevent them from realizing their potential as an athlete?

If this young man (and others like him) were allowed to rewrite the rules of the game and the disciplines of the team based on his own whims and desires . . .

what would happen to his team?

what would happen to the game of basketball?

20. Anyone with any experience in basketball would know intuitively that the young man in the above example is simply unreasonable or irrational. His wants and desires are simply incompatible with the game of basketball. Yet how many people feel they can operate on the very same attitude when it comes to important decision making that affects not only their well-being on earth, but their very salvation? For example . . .

> It has been proven that if someone drops out of high school, that decision will cost that individual more than $1,000,000.00 in lost income over his or her lifetime. Yet large numbers of students never finish high school. Why?

> According to the Census Bureau, over 70% of the poor in the United States are unwed mothers with children. Yet every year, untold thousands of girls and women get pregnant with no plans whatsoever of marrying the father. Why?

> Back in Question #12, we saw an extensive list of sins that St. Paul tells us will land us in hell. He warns us clearly that those who engage in *"immorality, impurity, licentiousnes, idolatry, sorcery, enmity, strife, jealousy, anger, selfishness, dissension, party spirit, envy, drunkenness, carousing, and the like"* will not inherit the kingdom of heaven. Yet for many people, fornication is a "lifestyle choice." People have many justifications and rationalizations for staying angry, holding grudges, and refusing to associate with others for trivial reasons. And, well, everyone gets drunk and gets a little rowdy now and then, so what's the hurt? Why is it that any rational person will accept the rules of basketball, but that same person would see nothing wrong with getting drunk at a wild party and then going to someone's home they met at that party and having sex with them?

> Why would the same person who insists that his own son learn and abide by the rules of the game refuse to speak to his own brother because the brother got something from their deceased parents' estate that he wanted?

VI. MAN IS RESPONSIBLE FOR THE GOOD OR EVIL OF HIS FREE ACTS

21. On the surface, it may appear that since human beings are by our very nature limited in knowledge and wisdom (ignorance), that we would also not necessarily be responsible for most of our actions most of the time. *The Catechism of the Catholic Church* states: *Imputability and responsibility for an action can be diminished or even nullified by ignorance, inadvertence, duress, fear, habit, inordinate attachments, and other psychological or social factors* (CCC 1735).

    Yet the *Catechism of the Catholic Church* also states: *This ignorance can often be imputed to personal responsibility. This is the case when a man "takes little trouble to find out what is true and good, or when conscience is by degrees almost blinded through the habit of committing sin. In such cases, the person is culpable for the evil he commits"* (CCC 1791).

    So, while mankind will always be plagued with some degree of ignorance most of the time, what is our responsibility in regards to our free acts?

MARK AND MADDIE RESPOND

Dear Stuck —

You are certainly to be commended for keeping your parents informed of your whereabouts. In fact, we are willing to bet that if you compared your "freedom" with that of some of your friends who are not as considerate of keeping their parents informed, you will find that either they are less trusted, or their parents are more stressed! But it all comes down to a question of responsibility. Quite simply, you cannot be allowed "to be on your own" because you are neither legally nor morally ready to be totally responsible for your own actions. And "being on your own" is not all it's cracked up to be. In order to earn the right "to be on your own," you will have to get educated to some degree, get a job, and start paying all of your own bills. Once you are self-supporting, only then can you be self-determining. It is a rewarding part of adult life, but it is also exhausting! For now, enjoy your time at home; you have so little of it left. Your parents will not be around forever, and sooner than you think, you will have all the opportunity in the world to call your own shots as you assume responsibility for yourself and your family for the rest of your life.

 God's blessings!

 Mark & Maddie

36. We are obligated by the Fourth Commandment to obey all lawful authority. Yet the State can and has passed unjust laws, such as those legalizing abortion, euthanasia, same sex "marriage," etc. In such cases, for the individual, what has the final word?

37. Does violating an unjust law on the authority of one's conscience protect one from civil prosecution for violating the law? Can you cite an example to back up your answer?

X. DISTORTION AND DEGRADATION OF PERSONAL CONSCIENCE

38. Those who study human development are proving further each day scientifically what the wisdom of the ages has known for centuries. Namely, that what a child experiences in the first few years of his life will have far-reaching consequences in his moral decisions for the rest of his life. Yet a right, or correctly formed conscience, can still be corrupted later in life. List seven possible causes for a corrupted conscience.

a.

b.

c.

d.

e.

f.

g.

MARK AND MADDIE RESPOND

Hey Melinda —

This is Maddie. Mark is sitting this one out. You know guys and weddings—they just don't understand, do they? I am really sorry to hear that people are not listening to you. What you are living through is a perfect example of the fact that no matter what we do (in this case your sister), other people are effected. By your confusion and your mother's tears, this should be evident. The reason why everyone is so upset is that your sister has done a masterful job of pitting the good consciences of you and your parents against the feelings of affection you have for her. But, Melinda, no one has the right to violate your conscience! And a decision on one person's part (in this case your sister) to violate God's moral laws, does not make an obligation on someone else's part (in this case you and your parents) to participate in it. And I really have to give your parish priest credit for standing his ground. It seems that so many priests just look the other way in situations like this.

Perhaps a solution to your difficult spot would be to skip the wedding as you have suggested, but go to the reception for a while. Give your sister a nice card telling her that you love her, and that you hope the best for her. As you pointed out, there is a very high probability that she will be divorced in a very short time, and she will really need your support then.

You have a wisdom that is past your years, dear. Stick to your values, and that white dress will really mean something at YOUR wedding! I will keep you in my prayers.

Maddie

Name _____

Date _____

Hour _____

Chapter 6: Morality and Action

Dear Mark and Maddie —

There is a new guy in school who I will call "Andy." He and I have been seeing a lot of each other lately and we have talked a lot. I know he came to our school to get a fresh start. He has had a lot of problems, and was even in a foster home for a while. I really think we are good for each other. At first I was alarmed at how easily he could shift from lies to the truth. But he has said that since being around me, he sees where he needs to change. The problem is that sometimes he asks me to do things that I know are wrong. Last week, for example, he asked to see my geometry homework, because he couldn't get his done. And before that, he asked me to keep a small box in the trunk of my car for him for a couple of days and made me promise not to open it. I never opened it, and I am afraid of what might have been in it. All this has made me really uncomfortable. I know he is trying to make a better life for himself, and I want to help him, but at the same time things just aren't adding up. It would seem that as long as I am trying to do some good in helping him, "bending the rules" every now and then should be no big deal. Why then does it always seem like it is a big deal?

— Cindy

INTRODUCTION

1. After reading the Introduction, at what stage in life does it appear that people essentially begin to write their own destiny?

2. What is the significance of this in regards to the timing or moral and religious training for a person?

I. HUMAN ACTS

3. Which of the following is a human act, and why?

    a. "My beard is growing."
    b. "I am growing a beard."

II. THE COMPONENTS OF THE MORAL CHOICE

4. The components of moral choice are The Object, The Intention or End, and The Circumstances. Which of these are the most important and why?

A. THE OBJECT

5. What exactly is "The Object?"

6. List some simple examples of Objects (remember, Objects can be morally good, evil, or neutral).

7. Some actions, such as adultery, are always evil, no matter who does them and for what reason. Some actions are intrinsically good, such as telling the truth or respecting God's Name. How do we know these actions are good or evil?

THE INTENTION OR END

The text uses the example of a good object or act (giving money to the poor). This act is then either kept good, by doing it for a good reason (to help the poor person), or it is made evil by doing it for a bad reason (the person giving the money is looking for human praise). Give your own example of a good act that has a corresponding good intention so that the integrity of the act is preserved.

Give an example of a good act that is ruined because of evil intentions.

Give an example of a morally bad act having the guilt attached to it reduced because of a good intention attached to it (Hint: Re-read the letter from Cindy at the beginning of this chapter).

CIRCUMSTANCES

The word "circumstance" comes from the Latin words *circum* and *stare* which mean . . .

Explain the connection between venial and mortal sin.

III. THE PRINCIPLE OF DOUBLE EFFECT

Consider this example: Every year, a very small number (thankfully!) of children die or suffer other serious adverse reactions due to childhood immunizations for such diseases as measles, mumps, rubella, polio, smallpox, chicken pox, etc. And we know that every year, by requiring these vaccinations, we are consigning a small and unknown number of children to suffering and death. Sometimes the vaccine causes the very disease it is designed to prevent. And this is acceptable. Why? Because we are desiring to do good, and an over-all good is being accomplished. Surely, if we knew precisely *which* children would die from the immunizations, we would not inoculate those particular children. Explain how this situation fits the criteria of the Principle of Double Effect.

A. THE ACTION MUST BE GOOD IN ITSELF OR AT LEAST INDIFFERENT.

14.

B. THE AGENT MUST HAVE THE RIGHT INTENTION.

15..

C. THE EVIL EFFECT CANNOT BE THE MEANS TO THE GOOD EFFECT.

16.

D. THE GOOD EFFECT MUST BALANCE THE EVIL EFFECT.

17.

IV. THE OBJECTIVITY OF GOOD AND EVIL

18. Give an example of where you have heard someone say something like, "What is evil for you may be good for me" or vice versa.

19. A homosexual man confesses to his parents that he has a "partner" and that they are going to build a life together. His parents object that as a Christian he was raised to know better than that, and that while they will love him forever as their son, they will never celebrate his lifestyle. To this he responds that the Bible was written a long time ago, and that the same Catholic Church that used to prohibit girls from serving Mass and the eating of meat on Friday now permits these two things. It is just a matter of time, he reasons, until the Church wakes up to the fact that there are others like him and that their lifestyle choices will be accepted. Where is the young man erring in his reasoning? (Hint: Go back to the previous chapter and review the difference between Natural and Ecclesiastical Law.)

V. THE HISTORICAL ARGUMENT FOR MORAL OBJECTIVITY

20. The text uses the example of how a basketball cannot be changed into a baseball by giving it to a pitcher and telling him to throw it. Yet, it is common in the public forum for euphemisms to be used to dull our sensitivity to the moral quality of what those words really stand for. Some examples are used below.

Choice — It seems like a harmless word. Someone may choose to go to the mountains for their vacation, and another chooses the ocean. One person's choice in music is classical and another's choice is rock and roll. How have people with evil intentions co-opted this word?

Tolerance — This word has usually described the quality by which we learn to make a moral judgment and those things that are morally neutral should be tolerated, even if we do not personally care for them. For example, my neighbor may paint his house a color tha I do not like. That does not give me the right to retaliate against him. I will have to be tolerant of his tastes in paint color. How has this word been redefined by, for example, the gay activist community?

Alternative Lifestyles — Years ago, a man and woman who lived together before marriage were scorned by society. Two people of the same sex who were attempting to imitate a married couple were simply dismissed as unreasonable. How does the clever use of two seemingly neutral words "alternative" and "lifestyles" make this behavior acceptable in many people's judgment?

VI. SOME ERRORS DERIVED FROM ETHICAL RELATIVISM

Following are the teachings on abortion as found in *The Catechism of the Catholic Church* and *The Book of Discipline of the United Methodist Church 2004.* Read and compare the two and then answer the questions that follow.

From *The Catechism of the Catholic Church*:

2270   Human life must be respected and protected absolutely from the moment of conception. From the first moment of his existence, a human being must be recognized as having the rights of a person—among which is the inviolable right of every innocent being to life.

2271   Since the first century, the Church has affirmed the moral evil of every procured abortion. This teaching has not changed, and remains unchangeable. Direct abortion, that is to say, abortion willed as either and end or a means is gravely contrary to the moral law.

2272   Formal cooperation in an abortion constitutes a grave offense. The Church attaches the canonical penalty of excommunication to this crime against human life. "A person who procures a completed abortion incurs excommunication *latæ sententiæ*" (Code of Canon Law, canon 1398) "by the very commission of the offense" (Code of Canon Law, canon 1314), and subject to the conditions provided by Canon Law (See Code of Canon Law, canons 1323-1324). The Church does not thereby intend to restrict the scope of mercy. Rather, she makes clear the gravity of the crime committed, the irreparable harm done to the innocent life who is put to death, as well as to the parents and the whole society.

2273   The inalienable right to life of every innocent human individual is a *constitutive element of a civil society and its legislation.*

2274   Since it must be treated from conception as a person, the embryo must be defended in its integrity, cared for, and healed, as far as possible like any other human being.

Prenatal diagnosis is morally licit, "if it respects the life and integrity of the embryo and the human fetus and is directed toward its safeguarding or healing as an individual . . . It is gravely opposed to the moral law when this is done with the thought of possibly inducing an abortion, depending upon the results: a diagnosis must not be the equivalent of a death sentence" (Congregation for the Doctrine of the Faith, *Donum vitæ* I, 2).

2275   "One must hold as licit procedures carried out on the human embryo which respect the life and integrity of the embryo and do not involve disproportionate risks for it, but are directed toward its healing, the improvement of its condition of health, or its individual survival" (Congregation for the Doctrine of the Faith, *Donum vitæ* I, 3).

"It is immoral to produce human embryos intended for exploitation as disposable biological material" (Congregation for the Doctrine of the Faith, *Donum vitæ* I, 5).

"Certain attempts to *influence chromosomic or genetic inheritance* are not therapeutic, but are aimed at producing human beings selected according to sex or other predetermined qualities. Such manipulations are contrary to the personal dignity of the human being and his integrity and identity" (Congregation for the Doctrine of the Faith, *Donum vitæ* I, 6) which are unique and unrepeatable.

From *The Book of Discipline of the United Methodist Church 2004* Part IV Social Principles, ¶161 The Nurturing Community, Section J—Abortion:

"The beginning of life and the ending of life are the God-given boundaries of human existence. While individuals have always had some degree of control over when they would die, they now have the awesome power to determine when and even whether new individuals will be born. Our belief in the sanctity of unborn human life makes us reluctant to approve abortion. But we are equally bound to respect the sacredness of life and well being of the mother, for whom devastating damage may result from an unacceptable pregnancy. In continuity with past Christian teaching, we recognize tragic conflicts of life with life that may justify abortion, and in such cases we support the legal option of abortion under proper medical procedures. We cannot affirm abortion as an acceptable means of birth control, and we unconditionally reject it as a means of gender selection. We oppose the use of late term abortion known as dilation and extraction (partial birth abortion) and call for the end of this practice except when the physical life of the mother is in danger and no other medical procedure is available, or in the case of severe fetal anomalies incompatible with life. We call all Christians to a searching and prayerful inquiry into the sorts of conditions that may warrant abortion. We commit our Church to continue to provide nurturing ministries to those who terminate a pregnancy, to those in the midst of a crisis pregnancy, and to those who give birth. We particularly encourage the Church, the government, and social service agencies to support and facilitate the option of adoption (See ¶161.K.) Governmental laws and regulations do not provide all the guidance required by the informed Christian conscience. Therefore, a decision concerning abortion should be made only after thoughtful and prayerful consideration by the parties involved, with medical, pastoral, and other appropriate counsel." (*The Book of Discipline of the United Methodist Church, 2004.* The United Methodist Publishing House. Nashville, Tennessee. 2004. p. 102)

21. When, according to Catholic teaching, is abortion justifiable?

22. For how long has the Catholic Church held this teaching?

23. When, according to Methodist teaching, is abortion justifiable?

A. SITUATION ETHICS

24. Clearly, the official Methodist teaching on abortion is tainted by Ethical Relativism. How does the Methodist teaching betray the presence of Situation (Circumstantial) Ethics?

B. CONSEQUENTIALISM

25. What about Consequentialism?

C. PROPORTIONALISM

26. Is Proportionalism present?

27. We can see why the Methodist teaching may be attractive to some, and indeed reflects the way a large number of people, including some Catholics, feel about abortion. It seems to offer everything without consequences. What it is lacking, however, is an over all ethic that champions life as the ultimate good. It is a situation such as this that St. Paul describes in Romans 3: 8 that we may never do evil (in this case, murder an unborn child) so that good (in this case save the life of the mother) may come of it.

Refer back to the case of the number of children dying from childhood immunizations. Our ethic of life in regards to little children is clear. We will tolerate the deaths of a few, in order to save the many and offer the prospect of a healthier life to many more. There are over 1,000,000 abortions in the United States every year. What evil would have to be tolerated to bring that number to zero?

MARK AND MADDIE RESPOND

Dear Cindy —

You are obviously a caring and empathetic person to reach out to Andy as you have done. And you also have a very perceptive conscience to sense the alarms that are going off with some of the activity and behavior he has been luring you into. Why does "bending the rules" seem like a big deal? Because it is a big deal! Even though you are wanting to do good, cheating is always bad. And allowing Andy to copy your geometry homework makes you just as guilty of the cheating as Andy is. And keeping secret packages for people is not only sneaky, it's downright dangerous! From a moral standpoint, your guilt for being involved in these behaviors is not as great as if you had known exactly what was going on, and then freely engaged in them anyway. That's why you feel that in a certain sense, what you are doing is okay. But the moral quality of your actions in and of themselves does not depend on your intentions. Cheating and sneaking are always wrong. That's why, as you say, "things just aren't adding up." Please keep trying to help Andy. It sounds like he needs it, and that you are a presence for good in his life at this time. But listen to your conscience. It sounds like you have a good one! In doing so, you will keep yourself out of trouble, and will no doubt give Andy some good example to think about and to imitate.

Christ's peace to you!

Mark & Maddie

Name _____

Date _____

Hour _____

Chapter 7: Sin and Conversion

Dear Mark and Maddie —

I am sixteen years old and my older sister is seventeen. I have a pretty good part-time job. A while back, my sister asked me if I would loan her some money, and when I asked her what for, she just said it was personal. We have always been pretty close, and she wasn't asking for that much (she doesn't work) so I gave it to her. I later found out that she was using the money for birth control pills and condoms. I know her boyfriend, and have never really liked him, but I figured my sister's friends were her business. Once I told her that now that I knew what she was doing with the money, that I would not loan her any more, she threatened to tell our parents. Then she demanded more money! What should I do? Was it wrong for me to give her the money to begin with? What if my parents find out?

— Phillip

INTRODUCTION

A. ALL PHYSICAL EVILS ARE THE RESULT OF ADAM'S SIN.

1. Perhaps you have thought, after seeing devastation suffered by innocent people as a result of some natural disaster, that God is somehow unfair. It makes sense that a drug addict might die from an overdose, but why do innocent children die as the result of an earthquake or tsunami? Explain the relationship between physical evil and Original Sin (for some help, see Wisdom 1: 12-16).

B. MORAL EVIL IS ALWAYS FREELY COMMITTED AND CAN ALWAYS BE AVOIDED. A PERSON IS THEREFORE GUILTY OF SIN IF HE CHOOSES MORAL EVIL.

2. The text cites Socrates in claiming that a given sin will hurt the sinner worse than the victim of that sin. How is this so?

3. Below, put a "P" in front of each example of a Physical Evil and an "M" in front of each Moral Evil.

_____ A teenage boy and girl have sex and the girl gets pregnant.

_____ The child of the couple described above lives in an environment of poverty and abuse.

_____ A drought brings starvation and disease to a poor tribe.

_____ A woman gets drunk, wrecks her car, and suffers severe injuries.

_____ A man spends hours devouring pornography on the internet.

_____ A girl is date-raped by her boyfriend who spends hours devouring pornography on the internet.

_____ Political maneuvering between rivals causes a disruption in food supplies that cause others to starve.

_____ A family is killed when their mini-van is struck by a drunk driver.

I. DEFINITION OF SIN

A. SIN IS ANY DEED, WORD, OR DESIRE AGAINST ETERNAL LAW.

4. Why do you think that Jesus issues such strong warnings about sins of the mind (See Matthew 5: 27-30 and Mark 7: 20-23)?

B. SIN IS THE VOLUNTARY TRANSGRESSION OF THE DIVINE MORAL LAW.

5. Name the other two positive laws that derive their legitimacy by their participation in the Divine Moral Law.

    a.

    b.

C. SIN IS A TURNING AWAY FROM GOD, TO CREATURES, IN A DISORDERED WAY.

6. What is the technical meaning of the word "creatures" in this definition?

7. In general, how does this definition describe human sinfulness?

8. This describes the root sin of _____.

II. THE REAL MEANING OF SIN IN THE BIBLE

9. The text tells us that the most common way of understanding sin in the Bible is in terms of "deviance" or "to lose the path." Most of us probably understand sin in terms of a crime with a corresponding punishment. And there is certainly that aspect to sin. Re-read Genesis 3: 1-7. Are the first man and woman intentionally trying to anger or directly defy God? Why do they disobey him?

III. SIN AS A PERSONAL ACT

10. Read the excerpt from *Reconcilatio et pænitentia*. It describes how human freedom must be held up as an inviolable and absolute value even to including allowing people to take personal responsibility for sins committed. In each of the following examples, explain the intention behind the action (which is probably good) and how the action denies the agent the possibility of being responsible for his or her actions.

   • A public high school builds a child care center to provide day-care for the illegitimate children of the un-wed mothers who attend the school.

   • A judge orders a man into counseling, to join Alcoholics Anonymous, and to attend AA meetings at least three times a week as part of his probation from his second conviction of driving under the influence of alcohol (drunk driving).

   • Weary of escalating deaths and injuries due to the misuse of handguns, a state legislature passes a law making the manufacturers of guns responsible for the damages that may be incurred when a gun is involved.

IV. THE LOSS OF THE MEANING OF SIN

11. The warning of the loss of conscience and the corresponding loss of a sense of the existence of sin are constant teachings of the Catholic Church. What are some examples that the text cites of this happening in our day?

A. CULTURAL AND ETHICAL RELATIVISM

12. The text states that in radio and television, music and conversation promote vices. Give some concrete examples of where you have seen this.

B. INCORRECT STATEMENTS OF MODERN PSYCHOLOGY

13. How much does it cost to spend an hour receiving therapy with a counselor?

14. How much does it cost to go to Confession?

15. Comment further on this, based on what your text says about sin and forgiveness.

C. THE CONFUSION BETWEEN MORALITY AND LEGALITY

16. The text uses divorce and abortion as two examples of immoral and sinful activities that are accepted in our society because they are legal. Can you think of any more? For example, go back to Chapter 1 (section VI-D) of this workbook, and re-read the First Amendment to the Constitution. How is the First Amendment misused to justify sinful activity in the name of "freedom?"

D. SECULARISM / HUMANISM

17. Many times religion, especially Catholicism, is criticized for making people feel guilty. One response to this has been to simply ignore God and any kind of religious limitations on life which is known as Secularism or Humanism. Once there is no sin, there is no guilt. In your own words, explain the dynamic that the text describes on page 122 regarding the consciousness of sin in our society.

V. DIVISIONS OF SIN

A. BY ITS ORIGIN: ORIGINAL OR ACTUAL

18. Original Sin and Actual Sin are taken away by the Sacrament of _____, whereas

    only Actual Sin is removed by the Sacrament of _____.

B. BY ITS GRAVITY: MORTAL OF VENIAL

19. A complaint made by some non-Catholic denominations about Catholic doctrine is the distinction that Catholic teaching makes between mortal and venial sin. Some say that all sin is just that: sin. To have varying gradations of sin is not correct. See 1 John 5: 16-17. What does the Bible say about mortal and venial sin?

20. For each example, write an "M" for a Mortal Sin and a "V" for a venial sin, and tell why you think the sin is mortal or venial.

    _____ A boy steals $5 from a bucket of change in his brother's room.

    _____ A couple of employees at a local discount store steal over $5,000.00 in merchandise as one commits the theft while the other keeps watch.

_____ A teenage girl misses Mass on Sunday because she is sick from being drunk the night before and just "doesn't feel like going."

_____ A fourteen-year-old boy opens a message in his e-mail and finds a pornographic image that he looks at for while, and then struggles with impure thoughts.

_____ A thirty-eight-year-old man regularly logs on to the internet, lookes at pornography for an hour and then masturbates.

_____ A wife, in a moment of frustration, lashes out at her husband for his lack of consideration of her needs.

_____ A wife, after much forethought, thinks of the most hurtful things she can say to her husband to "get back at him" for his lack of consideration of her needs.

21. In regards to the confession of sins, The Code of Canon Law (Ecclesiastical Positive Law) reads:

Canon 988 §1 Each of Christ's faithful are bound to confess, in kind and in number, all grave sins committed after baptism, of which after careful examination of conscience he or she is aware, which have not yet been directly pardoned by the keys of the Church, and which have not been confessed in an individual confession.

§2 It is recommended that Christ's faithful confess also venial sins.

Even though Church law requires us only to confess our mortal sins at least once a year, we are encouraged to "frequently" confess our venial sins. Why?

C. BY ITS INTENT: FORMAL OR MATERIAL

22. Looking back at Phillip's letter at the beginning of this chapter, as he did not know what she was spending his money on, would his loaning money to his sister have been a Formal or Material sin?

23. Now that he knows what she is spending the money on, if he were to loan her more, would the sin be Formal or Material?

D. BY ITS MANNER: COMMISSION OR OMISSION

24. The text cites Matthew 25: 1-46 (the whole chapter) as examples of sins of omission. Read that chapter. There are three parables that Jesus tells. The first is the story of the five wise and the five foolish bridesmaids. What is the moral of this parable?

The second is the Parable of the Talents. What is the moral of this parable?

The last Parable is the Judgment of the Nations. Which sin of omission does Jesus condemn in this parable?

E. BY ITS MANIFESTATION: EXTERNAL OR INTERNAL

25. External sins of words and actions are fairly easy to comprehend. Human experience shows us that internal sins of thoughts and desires are a little more difficult to isolate and understand. For example:

    - A young man notices a pretty young lady about his age. Simply taking note of an attractive person is no sin. How would this develop into a venial sin?

       How could it develop into a mortal sin?

    - A young woman is reflecting on a failed relationship. She acknowledges in her own mind that she bears part of the responsibility for the break-up, but that her former boyfriend was the major contributor to the problem. She wants to forgive him, but is having a hard time. She wonders if she is sinning since she has not yet forgiven him. Is she sinning? If not, why? If so, under what circumstances would her failure to forgive be sinful?

26. Along with avoiding sin, we are also required to avoid the occasions of sin. We say this at the end of the Act of Contrition. Give three examples of occasions of sin.

    a.

    b.

    c.

VI. COOPERATION IN EVIL

27. Match each situation with the term that best describes it.

____ Explicit Formal Cooperation   ____ Implicit Formal Cooperation

____ Immediate Material Cooperation   ____ Proximate Mediate Material Cooperation

____ Remote Mediate Material Cooperation

A. A student leaves his test exposed on his desk so that another may copy his answers.

B. People who grow and process illegal drugs for the dealers to sell on the street.

C. A student acts as a lookout for two others who are smoking behind a utility shed on school property.

D. A minor uses a fake ID to buy cigarettes for himself and his buddy who is also underage.

E. A man's retirement portfolio, which is managed by another agency, contains stocks of companies that promote pornography.

VII. EFFECTS OF SIN

28. The following is the actual text of a letter (with the name withheld to preserve privacy) that the author of this workbook received while writing it. It is from a twenty-year-old young man who is in jail for reasons that will become clear.

Dear Fr. Fred,

Thank you for your letter. It did lift my spirits, and I do pray to God a lot. I was just mest (sic) up on drugs and lost my way. I would like you to come and see me. I do not know what will happen, but I do have a good lawyer and I listen to her. I wish I could turn back time. But I know I can't and this I realize. I do have a lot to think about and to be thankful for, but it's hard. Father, I did not rape that girl, but I fear I may be found guilty regardless. But we are going to trial no matter what.

Thanks for writing,
(Name withheld)

PS. Remember when you use (sic) to tug on my ears? Nows (sic) one of those times.

America's prisons are full of people like this young man. How do they end up there?

What about *you*? Are there any areas of your life that include occasions of sin, or formal or material cooperation with sin that are weakening the grace of God that dwells within your soul? You no doubt have no intention of ending up in jail, but neither did anyone else who is there! What do you need to do to keep yourself on the straight and narrow?

VIII. CONVERSION AND FORGIVENESS

29. If someone dies in the state of mortal sin, (s)he goes to hell for all eternity. The soul of such a one is lost forever. While still on earth, under what circumstances is repentance not possible and a person a "lost cause?"

IX. THE SACRAMENT OF RECONCILIATION

30. Many people, including many Catholics, say words to this effect: "I don't need to confess my sins to a priest. If I tell God I am sorry in my heart, that's good enough." After reading this section, what might you tell such a person?

X. JUSTIFICATION

31. What do we do to deserve and then earn justification?

32. The Concept of Casuality.
    This section of the text has a lengthy citation from the Council of Trent regarding Justification (pp. 127-28). In it, the terms *final cause, efficient cause, meritorious cause, instrumental cause,* and *formal cause* are used. What do these terms mean? They are rooted in ancient Greek philosophy, and form a framework for understanding change in many things. Here the Council of Trent applies this framework to justification. We will try to undersand this by means of a comparison or analogy of a carpenter building a tool shed for storing his tools.

(continued next page)

- The carpenter or agent would be the *efficient cause*.

- The pile of lumber, door hardware, windows, and roofing material would be the *material cause*.

- The tools used to construct the shed would be the *instrumental cause*.

- Through the work of the carpenter, the collection of building materials (which is pretty much useless) takes on a new useful form as a tool shed. This would be understood as the *formal cause*.

- The need for a tool shed to store the carpenter's tools in the first place would be the *final cause*.

With this comparison in mind, what is the *efficient cause* of our justification?

How is Baptism the *instrumental cause* of our justification?

When the Council of Trent explains the *formal cause* of our justification, it makes a subtle but remarkable distinction that some Christian denominations have missed. Through the work of God, what happens to us?

XI. CONTRITION

33. A friend of yours has told you that he is planning to do some sinful act. You remind him that it is bad, but he responds, "Oh well, I'll just go to Confession afterward." What would you tell him?

34. What is "perfect contrition?"

35. What is "imperfect contrition?"

36. Is one bad and the other good, or is one good and the other better?

37. Below is an example of an Act of Contrition with two phrases set off in italics and labeled with a (1) and a (2). Read it and then identify where you find perfect and imperfect contrition.

    "O my God, I am heartily sorry for having offended you. (1) *And I detest all my sins because I dread the loss of heaven and the pains of hell.* But most of all, because (2) *they offend you my God who are all good and deserving of all my love.* I firmly resolve, with the help of your grace, to confess my sins, do my penance, and amend my life. Amen."

    a. Which part describes perfect contrition?   _____

    b. Which part describes imperfect contrition? _____

XII. CONVERSION

38. What is the root cause of conversion? That is to say, what is it that people finally come to understand that brings them to truly repent from sin, and seek to live as God's friends?

ADVANCED CONCEPTS

39. A number of scholars have proposed that having only two categories of sin (mortal and venial) is somehow deficient. Briefly explain how such academicians would describe . . .

    Mortal Sins

Grave or Serious Sins

Venial Sins

40. In Catholic writing and teaching that is true to the Magisterium, when referring to the type of sin that completely separates man from God, the terms _____, _____, and _____ all mean the same thing.

41. Why has the Magisterium of the Church rejected this three-fold division of describing sin? (For a hint, see 1 John 5: 16-17)

MARK AND MADDIE RESPOND

Dear Phillip —

It is always hard when people we love and trust betray us. You kind of give yourself away in your letter. You know what you need to do. You clearly should not loan (by the way, if your sister is not working, how is she supposed to pay you back?!) or give your sister any more money. You might also "beat her to the punch" by telling your parents what is going on yourself. Better that they hear it from you, don't you think? Also, since you did not know what your sister was doing with the money, while you cooperated in a bad act, you are not responsible for it, if that's any consolation. One other thing to consider: You said you don't like her boyfriend. It could be that deep down, neither does she. Bringing this out in the open between the two of you and your parents may be exactly what she needs to dump this guy and find someone else who will treat her better.

Write us back and let us know how things turned out.

Mark & Maddie

Name _____

Date _____

Hour _____

Chapter 8: The Ten Commandments and the Eight Beatitudes

Dear Mark and Maddie —

I have an aunt that I have always been close to. She and my uncle are my godparents. I don't know what happened, but she really went over the deep end! She started going to a "non-denominational" Bible study and now has a completely different group of friends. She quit going to Mass about eight months ago and demanded that my uncle and cousins join her at her new church. When they refused, she just left them. She said the Catholic Church has "too many rules," and that the churches of the "free traditions" respect the feelings of their members. I agree the Catholic Church has a lot of rules, and I don't understand a lot of them, but I can't see changing my religion over them? I feel so sorry for my uncle and my cousins. What can I do?

— Katie

INTRODUCTION

1. The text tells us that Christianity has new elements—foundations and principles—that are not founded on human reason alone, but are revealed to us by God. Give some examples of each below.

Elements of the Christian Faith We Know From Reason	Elements of the Christian Faith We Know From Revelation

I. THE TEN COMMANDMENTS

2. Another name for the Ten Commandments is the _____ which means "the ten words."

3. The text reminds us that the people of Israel knew that their destiny, for better or for worse, was tied to the fulfillment of the Ten Commandments. What about us to this day? Disregarding the spiritual benefits of obeying God for now, in simple *economic* terms, how would we benefit from obeying the Ten Commandments? That is to say, economists, government agencies, and the like, often compile data showing that such things as smoking, obesity, and failure to use seat belts cost the economy many billions of dollars per year. Pick out one or two of the Ten Commandments, and show how, if they were obeyed, our economy would save many resources.

II. THE CODE OF THE COVENANT

4. This section ends with the statement, "The fruit of fidelity is every person's goal—happiness." This would seem to conflict with much of what we hear in the public forum. For many people "happiness" consists in doing whatever you want. How would obeying God's laws bring us happiness? (For some hints, refer back to Question #3 and review Chapter 3: Freedom and the Moral Act.)

III. THE ETHICAL CONTENT OF THE TEN COMMANDMENTS

5. At the time that God gives the people of Israel the Ten Commandments, he does not yet demand great ethical requirements of them. Why?

6. When does God begin to demand more of his people?

7. How does God continue to reveal to us his ever developing ethic for living that is for our good? (Hint: How does the Bible treat such things as slavery and the death penalty as opposed to how we understand these issues today?)

IV. THE TEN COMMANDMENTS AND THE NATURAL LAW

8. We have studied much about law and the commandments. It is often cited by those who embrace moral relativism and secular humanism that the Bible is unreliable as a repository of truth. One might claim, for example, that we cannot look to the Bible for law regarding marriage, because polygamy was common in the Old Testament. Since marriage law has changed in the Bible, why should we pay attention to the biblical prohibitions against divorce and re-marriage, or a "marriage" between two people of the same sex? The Law of Moses says that Jews cannot eat pork or shellfish. It requires males to have the foreskin of their penis surgically removed (circumcision), and Christians are not required to pay any heed to these. How are we to know which parts of the Old Testament to obey and which parts to ignore? How do we even know the Ten Commandments are still valid? The answer is found in the Natural Law.

What is the point of intersection (?) between the Natural Law and the Law of Moses? That is to say, what is the main thing these two laws have in common?

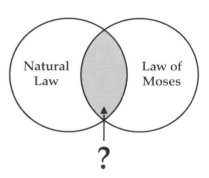

9. How would this explain that Christians are obliged to refrain from adultery, while ignoring the dietary codes of the Law of Moses?

V. DEVELOPMENT OF CHRISTIAN MORALITY
IN VIEW OF THE TEN COMMANDMENTS

10. The Ten Commandments are the framework upon which sound moral teachings can be understood. Once we have learned the Ten Commandments, what is the great motivator to help us to live out the ethic that Jesus taught?

11. Catholic apologist and author Gilbert Keith (G.K.) Chesterton once wrote:

    "... the great ideals of the past failed not by being out lived (which must mean over-lived), but by not being lived enough. ... The Christian ideal has not been tried and found wanting. It has been found difficult; and left untried." (*What's Wrong With the World.* 1910 Dodd, Mead, & Co., Reprinted by Ignatius Press. 1994. pp. 36-37)

    Based on what you read in this section, explain what Chesterton is saying in this citation.

VI. THE PRECEPTS OF THE CHURCH

12. Write the Precepts of the Church as they are found in the *Catechism* (nos. 2042-2043).

    a.

    b.

    c.

    d.

e.

13. Apply the Precepts of the Church. How do we live them?

a.

b.

c.

d.

e.

VII. THE TEN COMMANDMENTS AND THE BEATITUDES

14. The word "beatitude" comes from a Latin word meaning _____.

15. How do the Beatitudes take us beyond the Commandments and lead us to perfection?

VIII. THE MORAL VALUE OF THE DECALOGUE AND THE BEATITUDES

16. Pope John Paul II explained the connection between the Beatitudes and the Ten Commandments on page 145 of the text. What is this connection?

MARK AND MADDIE RESPOND

Dear Katie —

We are sorry to hear about the difficulties that your godparents and cousins are going through. Many people mis-understand the role of law in our life. Many people think laws are an infringement on their freedom, when in fact the laws are preserving their freedom. Your aunt's complaint about the Catholic Church's rules is common. When people complain to us about how they do not like the Church's rules, we always ask them specifically which rules they are so upset about. Funny how people can never answer that question. Ideally, Katie, the various rules the Church teaches are meant to bring us closer to God and enable us to live in peace with each other. The problem is that even many adults are not ready for the true freedom that living the way Jesus wants us to live brings to us. What is really sad is that new churches spring up every day that will never challenge their members to be responsible for their actions. As you have observed, the so-called "free traditions" have teachings that remove the consequences and responsibility for our actions. Jesus calls us to love, and then to act out of that love. And that is the essential core of all of Catholic teaching. What can you do? Be patient and kind to your aunt. Many times when people leave the Catholic Church like your aunt did, they make a lot of noise as to why they are leaving. But many times they also want to come back after being disillusioned by their "new church." Your being kind to her can show her that the welcome mat is out for her. You don't say what kind of a relationship you have with your cousins. Try to be available to them. And for yourself, take the time to study what the Church teaches, and more importantly why it teaches what it does.

We hope this helps.

> *Christ's peace to you.*
>
> *Mark & Maddie*

Chapter 9: The Social Teachings of the Church

Dear Mark and Maddie —

Our youth group at church is about to split down the middle! Some of the kids want to go on a mission trip to Guatemala this summer. Supposedly, we would pay for some simple building materials and then go to a small village in the mountains and help build a school building for about a week, and then come home. It would mean raising thousands of dollars to pay for airplane tickets and other travel expenses, as well as buying the building materials. I understand how this could be a good experience, since our parish is in a rather well-off suburban area. None of us kids have ever seen what real poverty is. The problem is that some of my friends and I, and our parents, think this is a big waste of money. We think that if we are going to raise all that money, we should just send what we would spend on airplane tickets and other travel expenses to some established missionaries in Guatemala (or wherever it might be needed), and then our youth group could volunteer to do some service work locally. I did some research, and the cost of one ticket is more than the average Guatemalan makes in a year! If one or more of us wanted to go down there and work for a year or so, I think that would be worthwhile. But honestly, I don't see how spending three or four days with some poor people, and then making a hasty retreat back to the comforts of America is going to teach us anything, and I doubt it is really going to benefit the people down there. What do you guys think?

— Ted

INTRODUCTION

1. What is the definition of "justice?"

2. Pope Paul VI once said, "If you want peace, work for justice." What did he mean by this?

3. Subtopics of social doctrine include labor practices and working conditions, governmental policies that affect taxes, the military, education, family life, the poor, etc. Some people say that the Catholic Church has no business making comments on these affairs. How has the Church answered this in the past?

4. Why do you agree or disagree with this reasoning?

5. What does *social justice* require of us?

6. What does *solidarity* or *social charity* require of us?

I. THE FAMILY

7. The family is called the "domestic church." Why is this? (Think: If a child is brought up in a home where there is no patience and little kindness, and then hears at Mass that he must be patient and kind, how will he likely respond to this teaching?)

8. The text describes the home as a hierarchical body with the father as its _____

   and the mother as its _____.

9. The text also states that the mother and father are equal in dignity. If someone representing the Catholic Church were to try to explain this on one of the cable news channels in an interview, how do you think it would be received by the interviewer and the public?

10. The text describes several examples that parents can set for their children that are vital if the children are to grow up with good Christian values. What are some of them?

II. OBLIGATIONS OF NATIONAL GOVERNMENTS

11. _____ is the key virtue in securing the common good for societies.

12. The text lists seven duties that the political community (i.e., legislators, judges, and executives such as the President or the Governor of a State) has a duty to honor for the good of families. Reading this list should give rise to some questions. It should be clear that American laws and attitudes are not in keeping with these demands. After each duty of the State toward the family, explain how the State is either succeeding or failing, or how it could better secure these rights for families.

The freedom to establish a family, have children, and bring them up in keeping with the family's own moral and religious convictions.	
The protection and stability of the marriage bond and the institution of the family.	
The freedom to profess one's faith, to hand it on, and to raise one's children in it, with the necessary means and institutions.	

The right to private property, free enterprise, to obtain work and housing, and the right to emigrate.	
In keeping with the country's institutions, the right to medical care, assistance for the aged, and family benefits.	
The protection of security and health, especially with respect to dangers like drugs, pornography, alcoholism, etc.	
The freedom to form associations with other families and so to have representation before civil authority.	

13. Explain the principle of *subsidiarity*, and give an example of what it means.

III. INTERNATIONAL RELATIONSHIPS

14. How would an increase of the awareness of the Triune God enhance the beneficial cooperation between countries?

15. The text lists a number of practices that oppress poorer nations and keep them poor. Following are the words describing some of these practices. What do they mean?

    "abusive if not usurious financial systems"

    "iniquitous commercial relations among nations"

16. Is there anything *you* do, whether you can help it or not, to encourage these practices? (For a hint, look at the shoes on your feet or the car you drive.)

IV. THE ROLE OF WOMEN

17. In the past, some have tried to use the Bible to justify the domination of men over women. They cite Genesis 3: 16 which reads: "*. . . your desire shall be for your husband, and he shall rule over you.*" Why is it at least inaccurate and at worst dishonest to use this piece of Scripture in this way?

V. THE GOODS OF CREATION

18. How does poverty prevent people from knowing God?

19. If we were to compare what an average American consumes daily in energy, water, food, and the waste generated in this consumption, we would find that it would sustain three or four other people who are used to getting by on much less. It is hard for us to envision the scarcity that most people experience when we have a closet full of clothes and the closet floor is covered with shoes. That safe drinking water is unavailable to the majority of the world's population is unimaginable for us who dump hundreds of gallons of safe drinking water on our lawns, and sometimes take more than one shower per day. For us, it is normal. Take a hard look at your consumption patterns. Are you confusing needs with wants? Where can you reduce your consumption?

VI. LOVE FOR THE POOR

20. In his masterpiece, *The Brothers Karamazov*, Fyodor Dostoevsky's character Ivan Karamazov says:

> "I must admit," Ivan began, "I have never been able to understand how it was possible to love one's neighbors. And I mean precisely one's neighbors, because I can conceive of the possibility of loving those who are far away. I read somewhere about a saint, John the Merciful, who, when a hungry frozen beggar came to him and asked him to warm him, [John] lay down with him, put his arms around him, and breathed into the man's reeking mouth that was festering with the sores of some horrible disease. I am convinced that he did so in a state of frenzy, that it was a false gesture, that this act of love was dictated by some self-imposed penance. If I must love my fellow man, he had better hide himself, for no sooner do I see his face than there's an end to my love for him . . . The idea of loving one's neighbor is possible only as an abstraction: it may be conceivable to love one's fellow man at a distance, but it is almost never possible to love him at close quarters." (Book V, Chapter 4)

   a. How does Ivan's observation compare with the way Jesus lived his life?

   b. How does Ivan's observation compare with the way many of us deal with the poor? For example, review Ted's letter to Mark and Maddie. How are Ted's observations similar to Ivan's?

c. How do the "missionary efforts" of many church groups compare with the efforts of the late Bl. Mother Teresa and her order of nuns?

d. A common event to raise awareness for the plight of the poor is to have a rice and beans dinner, where a good number of people gather and eat a supper of rice, beans, and glass of water, while one or two in the group eat a steak dinner with all the trimmings. The idea is to illustrate that most people in the world eat a simple and for the most part inadequate diet, while a few feast on rich foods almost daily. What would be the benefit of such an activity?

e. How might this also be a very empty gesture? For example, some years ago, such an event was held in Hollywood. The elite of TV and movies showed up to eat rice and beans, decried the way the poor are treated, and then were whisked away in limousines to five-star restaurants for their real meal of the evening that probably cost more than $100.00 a plate. What do you think of this and how might it apply to Ted's experience?

VII. RELATIONS WITH THOSE WHO ARE DIFFERENT

21. The text describes the breakdown of the "Protestant Ethic" in the years following World War II. With the moral and spiritual vacuum left by the demise of the Protestant Ethic, Fr. Richard John Neuhaus has claimed the time is ripe for "the Catholic Moment" in American life. Why might he claim this?

SUPPLEMENTARY READINGS

The spiritual and corporal works of mercy are not discussed much anymore. Read through them and then write an example as to how you can live out these virtuous works from the Gospel.

The Spiritual Works of Mercy

Counseling the doubtful	
Instructing the ignorant	
Admonishing sinners	
Comforting the afflicted	
Forgiving offenses	
Bearing wrongs patiently	
Praying for the living and the dead	

The Corporal Works of Mercy

Feeding the hungry	
Giving drink to the thirsty	
Clothing the naked	
Sheltering the homeless	
Visiting the sick	
Visiting the imprisoned	
Burying the dead	

MARK AND MADDIE RESPOND

Dear Ted —

You make some good points in your letter, and we certainly would not want to say anything that would discourage your group from reaching out to the poor. Like you say, for many of us in the United States, poverty—real poverty—is simply not part of our life experience. Maybe a trip like the one that is being proposed would help some of the members of your youth group to appreciate what they have. And let's be honest, a big part of the attraction of this project is the travel. Why not suggest a third alternative? Do what you propose: raise the large amount of money that would be needed for your trip to Guatemala. But then go on a smaller trip that could be done by car or bus to a destination in the United States where you could do some work to help the poor, and donate the difference to the mission overseas. You are right in that it does seem a bit excessive to spend the thousands of dollars that would be necessary for the air-fare and other travel expenses. This way, those who want to help the poor can do so, and you will also be helping other people overseas in the process. Let us know how things turn out.

Mark & Maddie

Name _____

Date _____

Hour _____

Chapter 10: The First Commandment
To Love God Above All Else.

Dear Mark and Maddie —

One of my friends had a slumber party a while back. Late at night, some of them decided to try to talk to the dead. One of the girls had a Ouija board, and they all sat in a circle and asked the board questions. They said that the dead would answer by where this thing pointed on the board. Is that true? Also, I had this feeling inside that as a Catholic I should not be around this kind of stuff. I don't know, I was just really uncomfortable. Did I do something wrong?

— Cecilia

INTRODUCTION

1. The text states, "The love of neighbor immediately follows the love of God because God calls us to love our neighbor to secure his love."

   In Matthew 6: 9-13, Jesus teaches his apostles The Lord's Prayer. Immediately following in vv. 14-15, Jesus says, *"For if you forgive men their trespasses, your heavenly Father also will forgive you; but if you do not forgive men their trespasses, neither will your Father forgive your trespasses."*

   If we must love our neighbor to secure God's love for ourselves, and if we must forgive others in order for God to forgive us, what does this say about such popular phrases as "God loves us unconditionally?" Are there, in fact, conditions for receiving God's love and forgiveness? Explain.

2. Often in art and iconography, the tablets of the Ten Commandments are often illustrated something like the one shown here. Why?

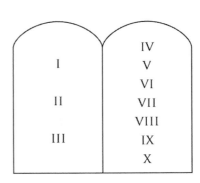

I. GOD, THE FOUNDATION OF HUMAN EXISTENCE: THE VIRTUE OF RELIGION

3. Name the two most significant times from the Bible when God has acted or intervened in human history in favor of his people as the Father of his children.

    a.

    b.

4. Jesus' name (Y'shua) means _____.

5. List the three Theological Virtues.

    a.

    b.

    c.

II. WORSHIP OF GOD AS A PRACTICAL EXERCISE OF THE THEOLOGICAL VIRTUES

6. When are the Theological Virtues given to us as a free gift from God?

A. FAITH

7. Write the definition of Faith as found in *The Catechism of the Catholic Church.*

8. Faith enables us to accept as truth things that cannot necessarily be proven scientifically, and reason is that which makes science possible. How do the two fit together?

9. We are to receive God's revelation with humility. What does "humility" mean?

10. We are also to cultivate what God has revealed to us intellectually. That is to say, we are expected to study our faith. It is for this reason that the Catholic Church dedicates enormous resources to Catholic grade schools, high schools, universities, and seminaries. Yet often, how do many Catholics fail in this regard?

11. What are some practical things we can do to safeguard our faith?

12. In regards to safeguarding our faith, what would be the prudent thing to do in regards to attending such activities as non-Catholic youth functions or Bible studies?

13. Which is by far the most effective way to communicate our faith?

14. Our understanding of faith is somewhat limited by our English language. Below are some nouns. After each word, write the verb (in the infinitive form) that corresponds to each noun.

    a. Hope   _____

    b. Love   _____

    c. Belief   _____

    d. Faith   _____

The Aramaic word for faith is *emet* which means _____. Aramaic is the language that Jesus, Mary, Joseph, and the apostles all spoke. For them, was faith a thing or an action?

15. Give a practical example of how someone might fall into sins against the virtue of faith.

Voluntary doubt

Involuntary doubt

Atheism

Heresy

Apostasy

Schism

B. HOPE

16. Write the definition of Hope as found in *The Catechism of the Catholic Church*.

17. How is the sin of despair a defect?

18. Give an example of how someone might fall into the sin of despair.

19. How is the sin of presumption an excess?

20. Give an example of how someone might fall into the sin of presumption.

C. CHARITY (Love)

21. Write the definition of Love as found in *The Catechism of the Catholic Church.*

22. Match the following examples of sins against love to the proper term.

____ Acedia   ____ Hatred of God   ____ Indifference

____ Ingratitude   ____ Lukewarmness

    A. Paul never really saw any results coming from his prayers. Seeing it as a waste of effort, he gave up on praying all together.

    B. Mayra went to Mass only when she felt like it and was often distracted by other things.

    C. Like many people, Miles has been so bombarded by foul language at work and in the movies that he doesn't speak out against it anymore.

    D. A college professor told his students to go out and enjoy all the sex they can while they're still young. "I did it," he proclaims, "and if I go to hell for it, it was worth it!"

    E. Lou Anne's father was in the emergency room with a heart attack. She prayed fervently to God for his recovery, repenting of her sins and promising God to live a better life. When he did recover, she went back to her old ways.

III. THE RELATIONSHIP BETWEEN THE LOVE OF GOD AND OF NEIGHBOR

23. Explain the relationship between love of God and love of neighbor. Which should come first?

IV. WORSHIP OF GOD: THE VIRTUE OF RELIGION

24. The texts reminds us, "Practicing this virtue [of religion] sometimes requires heroic effort, for secular society has become a hindrance to religious expression . . ." What have you personally seen in your life that backs up this statement?

V. SINS AGAINST THE VIRTUE OF RELIGION

A. IDOLATRY

25. Understanding the sin of idolatry is a major factor in understanding the Old Testament. The ancient Israelites were constantly tempted to worship the false gods of their neighboring tribes and kingdoms. In our day and age, it is unlikely that a Catholic is going to have a stone statue of some creature of fantasy that he considers to be his god. Yet idolatry is as rampant now as it was over 3,000 years ago with the ancient Israelites. How?

B. SUPERSTITION

26. It is not uncommon for someone to have some article that they consider "lucky." A man may have his "lucky fishing hat" or an athlete may have his "lucky pair of socks." Such things are always superstitious, but are they always sinful?

C. DIVINATION

27. What about the slumber party that Cecilia attended? In their attempted séance and use of a Ouija board (an attempt to make contact with the spirit world), did they commit a sin? Explain.

D. MAGIC

28. Magic and sorcery are both condemned as sinful in the New Testament (Acts 13: 6-12, Galatians 5: 20). (This is not to be confused with performances in which people do tricks with cards and pull rabbits out of hats, etc.) What have you seen in regards to magic and witchcraft in your community?

E. IRRELIGION

29. How might someone try to "tempt God?"

30. Clearly to vandalize a church or to desecrate a sacred image is sacrilegious. But what is probably the most common way people commit sacrilege?

31. Simony gets its name from Simon the Magician in Acts 8: 9-24, who offered St. Peter money if he would give Simon the power to call down the Holy Spirit, as St. Peter was doing when he administered the Sacrament of Confirmation. This is the biblical basis for the prohibition against buying and selling spiritual goods. Yet it is common practice for a family to give a priest money after he performs a baptism, a wedding, or a funeral. Is this simony? Explain.

VI. BIBLICAL CONDEMNATION OF ALL FORMS OF SUPERSTITION

32. In Ephesians 5: 5, St. Paul writes, "Be sure of this, that no immoral or impure man, or one who is covetous (that is, an idolater), has any inheritance in the kingdom of Christ and of God." What would be the "idol" to which St. Paul is referring?

MARK AND MADDIE RESPOND

Dear Cecilia —

You know in the Act of Contrition where we ask God to help us "avoid the near occasions of sin" and in the Our Father where we say "and lead us not into temptation?" The slumber party you are describing sounds exactly what those prayers are talking about! It sounds to us like it was probably all in fun, and maybe nobody took your efforts to conjure up the dead seriously. Maybe. The problem with this kind of stuff, dear, is that it can really open the door to some wicked, evil things. It sounds like your conscience is working fine. You felt uncomfortable, and that is good. You did not say if you actually took part in this activity or if you just watched. What was going on is objectively morally wrong. The variable is that due to ignorance, you don't sound like you would be culpable or responsible for what was happening. In the future, Cecilia, be very careful about what your friends are pulling you into. Keep going to Mass and receiving the Sacraments (especially Eucharist and Penance) to keep your conscience sharp, and you should be fine.

May God protect you always,

Mark & Maddie

Name _____

Date _____

Hour _____

Chapter 11: The Second Commandment:
YOU SHALL NOT TAKE THE NAME
OF THE LORD IN VAIN.

Dear Mark and Maddie —

One of my friends has this really annoying habit of beginning almost every sentence with "Oh my God!" or she puts some expression about God in almost everything she says. It's like, "Oh my God, did you see how much those shoes cost? Oh my God, that test was so hard! Oh my God, I can't wait till spring break. If I don't do better in geometry, I am in so much trouble with my parents, I swear to God!" See what I mean? I really like her as a person, but when she talks like that it really grates on my nerves. Isn't that like swearing or something? It's wrong isn't it? What can I tell her?

— Ashley

INTRODUCTION

1. In your experience of growing up, have you sensed any pressure or been told by word or example, of the necessity to develop your character so that people will know that when you give your word, nothing else is needed?

I. THE GRANDEUR OF GOD'S NAME

2. In English translations of the Bible, the word "lord" will appear in three distinct ways:
    * "LORD" in all capital letters, but with the "L" in a larger print font than the "ord" means that in the original Hebrew text the famous tetragram (the four letters) of YHWH was used. This is the mysterious Name of God that was revealed to Moses at the Burning Bush in Exodus 3: 14.
    * "lord" in all small letters is a title, such as the "lord of a house."
    * What does **Lord**, with a capital "L" mean?

II. OATHS

3. What is the definition of an oath?

4. The daily language of some people is laced with such phrases as, "I swear to God," or "God is my witness." Guided by the Second Commandment, what should be our attitude about such phrases?

III. OLD TESTAMENT DOCTRINE CONCERNING THE CUSTOM OF TAKING OATHS

5. What does the phrase, *in vain* mean?

6. In our times, when someone says they "took the Lord's name in vain," what do they usually mean?

7. In the context of the Old Testament, when people routinely called on God to witness assertory and promissory oaths, what would "taking the Lord's name in vain" have meant back then? Why would it be a sin to take God's name in vain under such conditions?

IV. NEW TESTAMENT DOCTRINE CONCERNING OATHS

8. Read the text from Matthew 5: 33-37 either from the Bible or from where it is reproduced in your text on pages 192-193. Jesus places a very heavy caution on the use of oaths. Normally, according to Our Lord, what should be sufficient in anyone's testifying to the truth of something?

V. NECESSARY CONDITIONS FOR THE LAWFUL USE OF OATHS

9. Karl gets in past his curfew, and knows he is in a lot of trouble for it because he has violated it four times in the past month. His parents have told him that if he misses his curfew again, they will take his car away for the rest of the school year. He quietly makes his way through the house, and slides into bed. The next morning his parents ask him if he was home on time, and he answers, "I swear to God, I was in bed twenty minutes before my curfew. I just forgot to wake you guys up." Comment on this situation. Is Karl guilty of a grave sin? Why or why not?

10. Was it necessary for Karl to take this oath?

11. Karl's little brother was up late that same night watching a DVD and saw him come in late. He tells his parents that Karl is lying, and Karl finally admits it, whereupon he loses his car, like his parents had promised. Consistent with his bad habit, Karl swears in his mind that he will get back at his little brother. Why would such an oath be invalid?

VI. VOWS

12. What is the definition of a vow?

13. What is the difference between an oath and a vow?

14. Review the conditions of a vow on page 194 of the text (promise, deliberate, and free). Below are the questions that a deacon, priest, or bishop asks of a couple before they exchange their wedding vows. Explain for which condition of the vow that each question is testing.

    • John and Sue, have you come here freely and without reservation to give yourselves to each other in marriage?

    • Will you love and honor one another as man and wife for the rest of your lives?

    • Will you accept children lovingly from God and bring them up according to the laws of Christ and his Church? (*This question may be omitted if the couple is past the age of childbearing.*)

15. How do marriage vows fit the description of the difference between an oath and a vow that you wrote in Question #13 above?

16. To review and summarize the difference between vows and oaths, fill in the following grid.

	Is made to . . .	Is witnessed by . . .
Oath		
Vow		

VII. THE IRREVERENT USE OF THE NAME OF GOD AND HOLY THINGS

17. What are some ways that we can publicly show signs of faith in a society that renounces religious signs?

18. It is not uncommon to see a famous person on television, who is living a very sinful public life, who is also wearing a crucifix in a necklace or some other piece of jewelry in the form of a Christian symbol. What do you think of this?

19. Consider ordinary people. How often do people get drunk, lie, steal, commit lewd sexual acts, or tear down their neighbor while all the time wearing a pair of earrings in the shape of a cross, or a St. Christopher medal or scapular around their neck? What do you think of this?

20. What about our homes? How many of us have a crucifix or an image of Jesus or his Mother hanging in our house, and right in front of these reminders of the omnipresence of God and the intercessory prayers of his Mother, we exchange angry and hateful words with members of our own family? Comment on this.

VII. BLASPHEMY AGAINST GOD, THE VIRGIN MARY, AND THE SAINTS

21. What is a *diabolic blasphemy,* and where have you seen it?

22. What is the best immediate defense for someone who has fallen into the bad habit of committing acts of blasphemy?

23. Explain why St. Thomas Aquinas says that blasphemy can be a more serious sin than murder.

MARK AND MADDIE RESPOND

Dear Ashley —

You might want to have your friend review the Second Commandment. Whether she knows it or not (we think she doesn't, but has just adopted a bad habit), every time she uses one of those phrases she is calling upon God to witness to the truth of the cost of the shoes, the difficulty of the test, or the amount of trouble she is in with her parents. It is not so much a question of whether what she is doing is wrong, but whether it is necessary. People can and do call upon God to witness to the truth of what they are saying, and given the proper circumstances, that can be a good practice. But your friend seems to have slipped into a bad habit of using God's name as an interjection. Maybe you can encourage her to find a different figure of speech. The danger here is that she would become so accustomed to using God's name in a sloppy way, that she may start to become careless about the proper reverence due not only to God, but to the Church, Mass, and other holy things. Most people have no idea what they sound like to others. Maybe you can help her in this regard.

Thanks for writing and God's blessings,

Mark & Maddie

Name _____

Date _____

Hour _____

Chapter 12: The Third Commandment:
REMEMBER TO KEEP HOLY THE SABBATH DAY.

Dear Mark and Maddie —

I am having a hard time with this whole Sunday Mass thing. It is supposed to be a celebration, but we are required to go or else it's a mortal sin. How can that be a celebration? Also, when I go to Mass, I see a lot of people sitting in the back rows, reading the bulletin and then they go to Communion and then head right out the door. They don't seem to be celebrating! It all seems so hypocritical to me. I like going to Mass sometimes. I like to sing, and the Eucharist means a lot to me. But sometimes I feel a lot closer to God when I am by myself than in a church full of people who seem a lot more interested in the whole thing getting over with than they are in worshipping God. Am I wrong in this? I am interested to hear what you have to say.

— Amy

INTRODUCTION

1. For most Christians, Sunday is the day of the week dedicated to the worship of God. For Jews, the day is _____, and for Muslims it is _____.

2. It was _____ who officially transferred the day of Christian worship to Sunday.

I. THE IMPORTANCE OF THE SABBATH IN THE OLD TESTAMENT

3. On page 205, the text cites two pieces of Scripture (Exodus 20: 8-11 and Leviticus 23: 3) which describe the two-fold purpose of the Sabbath. What are they?

    a.

    b.

4. As time went on in the centuries before Jesus' birth, the religious leadership of the Jews, for understandable reasons, began to multiply the number of laws and regulations regarding the Sabbath to the point where it had become impossible to obey them. Jesus strongly denounced this as he proclaimed, *The sabbath was made for man, not man for the sabbath*" (Mark 2: 27). What does Jesus mean by this?

II. THE LORD'S DAY IN THE NEW TESTAMENT

5. The text states that we know that the earliest Christians practiced the Jewish form of worship and the Christian liturgy simultaneously. What would this have looked like? (Keep in mind the two different days for worship for the two religions.)

III. THE CHRISTIAN SUNDAY

6. Why were celebrations of the Eucharist private until the year A.D. 314?

7. Many Catholic homes have Catholic calendars hanging in the kitchen or near the telephone. These calendars are full of feast days commemorating various saints and events in our faith. The calendar was not always this full of special days. How did the Christian calendar begin to be formed?

IV. OBLIGATIONS OF ATTENDING HOLY MASS ON SUNDAYS AND HOLY DAYS OF OBLIGATION

8. List below the ten Holy Days of Obligation as found in the Code of Canon Law, then place an "X" for those which are transferred to the Sunday following their actual date in the United States, and those that are not obligatory in the United States.

	Feast Day	When it is celebrated	Transferred to Sunday*	non-obligatory*
1.				
2.				
3.				
4.				
5.				
6.				
7.				
8.				
9.				
10.				

* in the dioceses of the United States

V. FULFILLMENT OF THE PRECEPT OF ATTENDING MASS

9. What are the three examples given in *The Catechism of the Catholic Church* as valid reasons for missing Mass on Sunday?

10. Pope John Paul II always referred to the Jews as "our older brothers." Since Christianity was born of Judaism, it only makes sense that there would be certain Jewish practices that have survived in our Catholic faith. One such practice is the vigil celebration. Jews have always celebrated special feast days from sundown the day *before* the feast day until sundown the day of the feast day. For this reason, it has always been the Catholic custom to celebrate feasts accordingly. For example All Hallow's Eve (*All Hallow Even* in Old English, or our current term Halloween) was when people began the great feast of All the Holy Ones (All Hallows) or the vigil of All Saints. To this day, it is the practice in most all parishes to offer vigil Masses every Saturday evening for the Masses on the following Sunday, and to have vigil Masses the evening before the various solemnities and Holy Days of Obligation. While this is certainly an authentic expression of Christian Tradition, what should the faithful avoid in attending vigil Masses.

11. The text states that if we can fulfill our Sunday Mass requirement if we attend a wedding or a funeral Mass on Saturday afternoon or evening. If a Saturday afternoon or evening wedding or funeral Mass is to fulfill the requirement, what conditions must be met?

VI. THE OBLIGATION TO REST

12. What are two possible negative results of ignoring our need for rest?

    a.

    b.

VII. ACTIVITY PERMITTED ON SUNDAY

13. What would be some examples of work that would not only be allowed, but would be necessary on Sunday?

14. What are some examples of work that does not have to be done on Sunday? That is, work that, with proper planning, could be done the day before, or postponed until the following week?

VIII. RE-CHRISTIANIZATION OF SUNDAY & CONCLUSION

15. Some people remember when, in American society, Sundays were distinct from the rest of the week. Most businesses were closed on Sundays and people spent the day visiting family and relaxing. It is not uncommon for such people to blame the business community and "corporate greed" for the fact that all the stores are open on Sunday, enticing people to shop and forcing others to work. What do you think of this situation and your own attitudes about keeping the Sunday rest?

16. What is the net effect on a Catholic who ceases to attend Sunday Mass?

MARK AND MADDIE RESPOND

Dear Amy —

Sad to say, but most of what you say is true. Many people have no clue as to what a great gift the Mass is to us and what it means. And with this attitude is certainly is hard to see any aspect of a celebration. The important thing is for you to look inside yourself, and do what is right. The Third Commandment is quite clear, and so is the teaching of the Church. To miss Mass on Sunday without a good reason is a mortal sin. Missing Mass was a problem even as the New Testament was being written. The writer of the Letter to the Hebrews (10:24-25) exhorts his readers: "And let us consider how to stir up one another to love and good works, not neglecting to meet together, as is the habit of some, but encouraging one another, and all the more as you see the Day drawing near." The term "meet together" refers to the Early Christians gathering to celebrate the Eucharist. And, Amy, you might want to be careful about throwing the word "hypocrite" around. Every church every Sunday is filled with less-than-perfect people. In fact, the Church is not a resort for saints (that's what Heaven is); it is a hospital for sinners. As one holy priest once said, "Yes the Church is full of hypocrites, and I am probably the biggest one. The good news is that there is always room for one more, and you are most welcome to join us!" So keep going to Mass. Listen to the Word of God and reflect upon it. Receive Holy Communion with a sincere and humble heart. You can't help but to become a better person because of it!

Love and prayers,
Mark & Maddie

Name _____

Date _____

Hour _____

Chapter 13: The Fourth Commandment:
HONOR YOUR FATHER AND MOTHER.

Dear Mark and Maddie —

When my mom was in high school, her mom (my grandmother) abandoned her family in favor of a guy she met on the internet. My grandpa came home from work one day and found divorce papers on the kitchen table along with papers signed by grandma giving up her rights to her children, including my mother. He didn't have much choice, because grandma had already left for another state to be with her new "love." All of the family has a great respect for grandpa. He raised her and her sister and three brothers himself. Even though she never really talks about it, I can tell that my mom is still hurting from what her mother did to her. Does she still have to honor her mother like is says in the Ten Commandments? What's really hard is that my grandma has been calling my uncles and is trying to re-establish her relationship with her children. She hasn't called my mom yet, but I'm afraid that when she does, it is going to open a bunch of old wounds, and I don't want to see my mom get hurt anymore. Grandpa is just really quiet about it all. What kind of a response do all of her children and grandchildren owe her?

— David

INTRODUCTION

1. The Fourth Commandment specifies that honor is due from children to their parents. Taking the Fourth Commandment in context with the rest of the Bible, which other relationships are included in this law?

I. LOVE: THE FOUNDATION OF THE FAMILY

2. The text states that, "Christian morality is a morality of charity." In the Part I of the text, *Principles Of Moral Theology*, we studied such topics as law, morality, conversion, etc. Many times, people get so preoccupied with the laws and rules that they lose sight of the bigger picture. What, ideally, should all Catholics understand as the driving force behind the Ten Commandments, the Precepts of the Church, the Code of Canon Law, and teachings as those found in *The Catechism of the Catholic Church*?

3. The text describes familial love as "supernatural love." What does that mean?

4. This section ends with the statement, "The family is a privileged community . . ." What does "privileged" mean in reference to the family?

II. BIBLICAL FACTS ABOUT THE FOURTH COMMANDMENT

5. The Fourth Commandment is one of the two positive commandments and the only one that carries a promise of blessing to those who would obey it. This promise is repeated in many forms in the rest of the Old Testament. What is the blessing that is promised?

III. RELATIONSHIP BETWEEN SPOUSES

6. In our day, there has been much negative criticism of the Bible and of Christianity by those who make the accusation that the Bible and the Christian faith discriminate against women. They are quick to point out such passages as, "*²²Wives, be subject to your husbands, as to the Lord. ²³For the husband is the head of the wife as Christ is the head of the church, his body, and is himself its Savior. ²⁴As the church is subject to Christ, so let wives also be subject in everything to their husbands*" (Ephesians 5: 22-24) and then go on to claim how Christianity discriminates against women.

    But the text correctly cautions us against taking Scripture out of context (p. 223), and in fact if we read one more verse further, we find St. Paul admonishing husbands with these words: "*²⁵Husbands, love your wives, as Christ loved the church and gave himself up for her. . . .*" (v. 25)

    a. How exactly does Jesus show his love for the Church?

    b. What, then, is St. Paul demanding of husbands?

    c. Does St. Paul demand the same of wives towards their husbands?

    d. So, is there any "discrimination against women" in St. Paul's writings?

7. When St. Paul speaks of "love" he uses the Greek term *agapan* which means what?

IV. PARENTS' RELATIONS WITH THEIR CHILDREN

8. Many times in Christian writing there will be references to "the Apostle" with a capital "A". Who is this?

(Also, for future reference, many times reference will be made to "the Prophet" with a capital "P". Who is this?)

9. What are two negative trends in current society regarding the relationship between parents and their children?

    a.

    b.

10. In the Rite of Marriage, the deacon, priest, or bishop receiving the vows of the couple to be married asks them the following question (among others) regarding their readiness for marriage.

    Will you accept children lovingly from God, and bring them up according to the Laws of Christ and his Church?

    Later, when the parents bring their child to the Church for Baptism, the deacon, priest, or bishop performing the Baptism will ask the parents,

    You have asked to have your child baptized. In so doing, you are accepting the responsibility of training him (her) in the practice of the faith. It will be your duty to bring him (her) up to keep God's Commandments as Christ has taught us by loving God and our neighbor. Do you clearly understand what you are undertaking?

    a. List five practical and real-life examples as to how parents bring up their children keeping "God's Commandments as Christ has taught us by loving God and our neighbor," "according to the laws of Christ and his Church."

        •

        •

-

-

-

b. It is common for couples who are living together in a life of fornication, who are avoiding pregnancy through the use of artificial contraception (birth control pills, condoms, etc.). Many intend on continuing the practice after marriage. They then present themselves at their local parish, seeking a "traditional Catholic wedding." Given the question about their willingness to accept children that they will be asked publicly, in front of God and all those gathered, explain what you think of this situation.

c. It is also becoming more common for unmarried couples to present themselves at the local parish asking for Baptism for their illegitimate child(ren). At the Baptism they will be asked, "*. . . you are accepting the responsibility of training him (her) in the practice of the faith. It will be your duty to bring him (her) up to keep God's Commandments as Christ has taught us by loving God and our neighbor. Do you clearly understand what you are undertaking?*" In their current state, are they in any position to be training their child(ren) in the way of the faith?

If a parent tells a child to do one thing and then the parent does another, which will the child follow, what the parent does or what the parent says?

Given their unmarried state, are these parents in any condition to teach their children to keep God's Commandments as Christ has taught us?

What should the priest or catechist in a parish do in such situations?

11. The text says that while both parents must participate in raising their children in the faith, studies show that fathers play an especially important role in forming their children's religious habits. Why do you think this is so?

12. Statistics show that more than one-third of American children live in homes without their father. Statistics also show a steadily declining number of people attending church on Sunday. Catholics are indistinguishable from other Christians in this regard. How might the two be connected?

V. CHILDREN'S RELATIONS WITH THEIR PARENTS

13. Sadly, not all parents measure up to the standards set forth by God in the Bible. Even King David was not a very effective parent! Children, especially adult children, of parents who failed in their role as mothers and fathers often wonder if they are breaking the Fourth Commandment because they do not feel any particular affection for their parents. How would you answer such a person?

VI. RELATIONS WITH OTHER MEMBERS OF THE FAMILY

14. Describe the shift that has taken place within families over the past few centuries.

15. How does the principle of *subsidiarity* apply to the needs of families (see 1 Timothy 5: 3-8)?

VII. OBLIGATIONS OF CIVIL AUTHORITY

A. CITIZENS' OBLIGATIONS TO GOVERNMENT

16. Young people often complain that those in authority "are out to get them." What advice would St. Paul have for such people? (Look up Romans 13: 1-7 in a Bible, or read it as reproduced on p. 227.)

17. Both Sts. Peter and Paul and Jesus himself tell us to obey civil authority. Yet historically, these authorities have sometimes engaged in arbitrary and even tyrannical activity. In such cases, Christians, and all people of good will, have the right to oppose, and if necessary, overthrow those who abuse their power. What is the measure by which a Christian knows if civil authority is being misused?

B. GOVERNMENTS' OBLIGATIONS TO CITIZENS

18. Why does public authority have power?

19. How does the *principle of subsidiarity* apply to the relationship between the State and families?

20. In your opinion, does the State abide by the *principle of subsidiarity*? Explain what you have seen.

MARK AND MADDIE RESPOND

Dear David —

What a sad story. Your grandfather sounds like a remarkable man. Your question can be answered a number of ways. When your grandmother gave up her rights over her children, as far as the law is concerned, she was dead in regards to her children. Now that everyone is an adult, adults are free to form friendships and relationships with whomever they please. If your grandmother wants to contact her adult children, and if they want to respond or to ignore her, they are free to do as they please. Our guess, however, is that you are not so much interested in the legal questions as the moral ones. So here goes. Your grandmother essentially wanted to make herself a stranger to her own family in favor of a third party she met over the internet. That is really despicable. But so are all of our sins that put Jesus on the cross. Jesus forgave His torturers while they were still torturing him! And that is the ideal to which we are all called. Can we do it? With God nothing is impossible, but for most of us most of the time, especially when there is such deep betrayal and pain, it will be very hard to do. For now, be polite. We don't think you are morally obligated to go out of your way to fawn all over this woman, but a little common courtesy never hurt anyone. Try to be pleasant. Who knows, things may work out. Eventually, they will have to work out, because none of us gets into heaven until all of us love each other every bit as much as God loves His own Son. Something tells us we will all be spending a lot of time in Purgatory making peace with those who hurt us and whom we hurt while we were here on earth. You might want to say some extra prayers and try to be extra helpful to your mom in the coming weeks.

    Mark & Maddie

Name _____

Date _____

Hour _____

Chapter 14: The Fifth Commandment:
You Shall Not Kill.

Dear Mark and Maddie —

Why is there so much attention and mercy given to criminals and killers? What about their victims? At Mass a while back, the priest was actually speaking against the death penalty in his sermon! He said the Pope teaches that the death penalty is wrong. I'll bet neither of them ever had a family member murdered. Does our Church really teach that the death penalty is a sin?

— Ben

INTRODUCTION

1. What is . . .

   a. *autonomy*?

   b. *heteronomy*?

   c. *theonomy*?

2. The Capital Sin associated with *autonomy* would be _____.

3. The Virtue associated with *theonomy* would be _____.

I. RESPECT FOR HUMAN LIFE

4. Killing an innocent person (including suicide) is a grave sin, contrary to which three entities?

    a.

    b.

    c.

5. It is sometimes proclaimed by certain individuals, "It's my life, and I'll do what I want." How is this attitude an affront to the Fifth Commandment? (For a clue, see Romans 14: 7-8)

II. CONSERVATION OF EXISTING LIFE

6. Everything we have is on loan to us from God. There are many pithy statements that people make to drive this point home. Such statements as, "You can't take it with you!" and "I never saw a hearse pulling a U-Haul® trailer!" are evidence that most people accept that our position, power, and earthly material goods do us no good once we are dead. Look up the following passages from Scripture.

    What is Jesus telling us in his parable in Matthew 25: 14-30 about the following?

    The amount of anything (talent, ability, beauty, etc.) that God gives to his children.

    The eternal consequences of doing all we can with what God has given us as opposed to "just getting by."

    What warning does St. Paul give in 2 Corinthians 5: 10?

So what is the point of all this? What happens to our attitude when we truly realize that all we have in on loan from God, and he will demand an accounting from us at the end as to how we managed his goods (e.g., compare *stewardship* to *ownership*)?

7. In the world today, as evidenced by the violence that is glorified on our movie and TV screens, the thriving pornography industry, the lucrative nature of the abortion industry, the trafficking in human beings as slaves and prostitutes, and global terrorism, it should be clear that the over-all value we place on human life is quite low. If we saw God as the absolute owner of our life and the lives of others, how would this be different?

A. THE DUTY TO CONSERVE ONE'S OWN LIFE

8. We are required to defend our own life against an unjust attacker.

   If an adult came at you with a large knife, and you were convinced this person intended to use the knife to kill you, and you had a gun on your person, how would you be allowed to legitimately respond to the attack?

   Assume you are the same person carrying the same gun, only this time it is a nine year old child who is angry at you and comes at you with a baseball bat. What force would you be allowed to use?

B. RESPECT FOR THE LIFE OF OTHERS

9. Aside form outright murder, what other three crimes are forbidden by the Fifth Commandment?

   a.

   b.

   c.

C. ABORTION AND THE RIGHTS OF THE UNBORN

10. All induced (i.e., brought about by human intervention) abortions are mortally sinful. List and describe the three classes of induced abortions.

    a.

    b.

    c.

11. If someone is excommunicated from the Church as the result of having or participating in an abortion, are they out of the Church forever? (This is not covered in the text. See *The Catechism of the Catholic Church* 1463 or consult a priest.)

D. THE ERROR OF A PRO-CHOICE CATHOLIC (i.e., "FOR A FREE CHOICE")

12. Explain the two arguments for abortion, as held by the "pro-choice" movement.

    a.

    b.

E. CAPITAL PUNISHMENT

13. Explain Catholic teaching in regards to the death penalty. Under what kind of circumstances is the death penalty allowed?

14. Why, especially in the United States, would Pope John Paul II's observation that the conditions that warrant capital punishment "are rare, if not practically non-existent."?

15. Go back to Question #8. According to Catholic teaching, the use of capital punishment is an extension of what other well-established right?

16. From the standpoint of the salvation of souls, why is capital punishment undesirable?

III. THE PROBLEM OF PAIN AND SUFFERING

17. What has been part of the cause of the rise of atheism in the world?

18. The central message of Christianity is that the suffering and death of Jesus on the cross makes up for, or pays the price for all the sins of the world. That's the Good News (the Gospel) because (1) we don't have to pay the horrible price ourselves, and (2) we are unable to pay the price even if we tried. Yet the Church has constantly taught that suffering, when united with the suffering of Christ on the cross somehow offers to God reparation for sin. St. Paul is the greatest champion of the teaching that the cross is sufficient, and that any other human efforts to add to what Jesus did are at best useless and at worst blasphemous. Yet, St. Paul himself writes, *"Now I rejoice in my sufferings for your sake, and in my flesh I complete what is lacking in Christ's afflictions for the sake of his body, that is, the church"* (Colossians 1: 24). Is this to say that the suffering of Jesus was insufficient? Complete the following diagram and indicate where our sufferings figure into atonement for our sins.

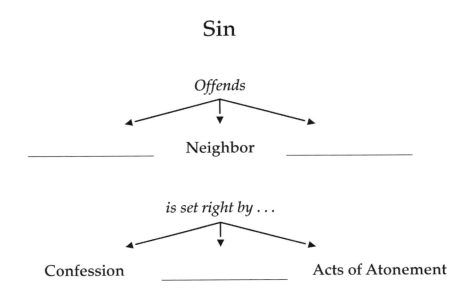

IV. THE MEANING OF DEATH

19. The Greek roots for the word *euthanasia* mean _____.

20. A common justification for euthanasia goes like this: "When my cat was old and suffering, I just couldn't bear to watch it so I took her to the veterinarian and he put her to sleep. Now, if I can show that kind of mercy to my cat, why can't I do so also for my father who is suffering the ravages of Alzheimer's disease?" What would be the Christian response to such a proposal?

21. Mark each of the following that would be euthanasia, or the direct killing (i.e., murder) of a sick or otherwise incapacitated person. Tell why you believe that it is euthanasia or why you don't think so.

_____ A ninety-year-old woman is suffering from pneumonia after falling and breaking her hip. All efforts to clear up the infection in her lungs have failed due to her age and poor overall health. The doctor gives her morphine so that she can rest. A side effect of morphine is that it depresses respiration. Some time after receiving the morphine, the woman stops breathing and dies.

_____ A young man dying from AIDS sees on the internet how a "cocktail" can be made from over-the-counter medications that will cause his heart and lungs to stop functioning. He has his "partner" go to the local drugstore and buy the medicines. With his "partner" present, he swallows the pills and dies some hours later.

_____ A teenage girl was drinking with her friends and tried to drive home. She was in a horrible accident and was not wearing a seatbelt. By the time she got to the hospital, she had lost a lot of blood. The surgeons did all they could, but came to the conclusion that there was simply no way to save the girl's life, so they ceased the operations they were doing and allowed her to die on the operating table.

_____ A man in his forties is severely mentally retarded. He requires constant care to help with his eating, getting dressed, and going to the bathroom. He is being taken care of by his younger sister. One day, he falls to the floor clenching his chest in pain. The sister concludes that he is having a heart attack. She goes down to the floor, where she holds him and comforts him, but never calls an ambulance. She reasons that he has suffered enough in this life, and allows him to die from the heart attack.

V. RESPECT FOR THE SOULS OF OTHERS: AVOIDING SCANDAL

22. What is scandal?

23. List the six provocations of scandal and the corresponding examples as found in the text, and then list one of your own with an example.

Cause for scandal	Examples
1.	
2.	
3.	
4.	
5.	
6.	
Your Example	

VI. JUST WAR

24. One of the demands of the Just War theory requires that non-combatants (i.e., the civilian population) be kept as safe as possible from the ravages of war. Modern "smart weapons" can be precisely aimed at military targets, and thus minimize damage to surrounding areas that may be civilian in nature. How would this be an advantage in executing a just war?

How might such weapons increase violence and destruction?

VII. RESPECT FOR THE BODY: MUTILATION AND ORGAN TRANSPLANTS

See the section on Sterilization which also describes common ways that people mutilate themselves.

VIII. CLONING

25. Explain how the cloning of plants or animals would or would not be morally objectionable.

26. One of the promises of human cloning is the possibility of growing new organs to replace failing organs. A sample of DNA would be taken from someone with, for example, failing kidneys, and then new kidneys would be grown and then transplanted to the original human. What are the moral implications of this?

IX. ILLICIT DRUG USE, SMOKING, AND THE ABUSE OF ALCOHOL

27. The Bible does not speak directly to issues such as smoking and illicit drug use. Biblical teaching does approve of the use of alcoholic beverages (See Psalm 104: 15 and 1 Timothy 5: 23), while at the same time condemning drunkenness as gravely sinful (1 Corinthians 6: 9-10, Galatians 5: 19-21). Nowhere does the Bible mention a minimum drinking age. Why then would it be sinful for an underage person to smoke or drink, and for any person to use illegal drugs?

X. STERILIZATION

28. Imagine a patient goes to his doctor and complains that when he sleeps on it at night, he wakes up and "it feels like a thousand needles are poking my arm." So, to avoid this pain, he requests that the doctor amputate his arm. How would any reasonable and ethical doctor respond, and why?

29. Imagine that a teenage boy goes to the doctor complaining that he is too small and too skinny. He asks the doctor to prescribe and to supervise his use of steroids so that he can build up his muscle mass, and so that he could achieve higher self-esteem and be more popular. How would the doctor respond? What might he recommend?

30. Imagine a man or a woman goes to the doctor requesting a vasectomy (for the man) or a tubal ligation (for the woman) because they don't want the worry of becoming pregnant. How would the doctor respond?

How is this inconsistent with what the doctor would do in Question #27?

31. Imagine a teenage girl goes to her doctor and says she wants to start having sex, but doesn't want to worry about getting pregnant, so she asks the doctor to put her on birth control pills, and to supervise her use of them. What would most likely be the doctor's response?

   How is this inconsistent with what a doctor would say to the boy who wanted steroids?

32. This chapter has laid out some teachings that are difficult for many people to understand. A sizeable percentage of the population at large favors abortion, euthanasia, and cloning. For the majority of the population, sterilization is not even an issue. Sadly, as a group, the opinions of Catholics are indistinguishable from those of the population-at-large. While it may be difficult to accept the Church's teachings on these and other issues, how might we discover the truth that these teachings contain?

SUPPLEMENTARY READINGS

Read *The Hippocratic Oath*. This is the oath that doctors take as they assume their role as healer. It is certainly a noble set of beliefs and values. Where is medicine in the United States coming up short when compared with this Oath?

MARK AND MADDIE RESPOND

Dear Ben —

The Church does not teach that capital punishment is a sin. It teaches that out of respect for all human life (including yours) the death penalty should only be used if it is the only way to protect innocent people from an unjust attacker. Certainly in our country, we can put someone in jail for life, and achieve that goal. But, Ben, we detect some high emotions in your letter regarding the death penalty. You are probably right, neither the Pope nor your parish priest have had family members who were murdered. But they do have a lot of experience with people who are trying to repent of their sins. It is a question of what our highest goals are and should be. If we want as many people as possible to get to heaven, then we need to make sure that everyone has every opportunity to repent of sin, and go back to God. If we execute someone, the chance for repentance dies along with the condemned person. Jesus certainly did not deserve what He got on Good Friday, don't you think? But your sins, our sins, and those of the murderer on death row all put Him on that cross. For this reason, everyone ought to have the chance to repent of the evil we have done, and become once again friends with God.

We hope this helps explain things a little.

Mark & Maddie

Name _____

Date _____

Hour _____

Chapter 15: The Sixth and Ninth Commandments:
YOU SHALL NOT COMMIT ADULTERY.
YOU SHALL NOT COVET YOUR NEIGHBOR'S WIFE.

Dear Mark and Maddie —

I know it's not just me, but that I speak for a lot of my friends when I say that I am sick and tired of being lectured to all the time about sex. It's like that's all we ever hear about at school, at church, and from our parents. I'll admit, I'm seventeen and I've had sex a couple of times. I kind of regret loosing my virginity, but it's not like it killed me or anything. It's not like I'm the only one who is doing it, and besides, I'm not hanging out with those guys anymore anyway. The way I see it, sex is natural and the human body is beautiful. Someone even told me that the Catholic Church even teaches that. Well, if they do, why are they always telling us not to do anything that has anything to do with sex? It's really hypocritical. I know you guys are both "holier than thou" so I suppose you will rip me open for writing this letter, but I am interested in what you have to say.

— Name withheld

INTRODUCTION

1. Chapter 15 is the longest chapter in the book. Why do you think this is so? (Hint: If this book were written 100 years ago, and you were studying it 100 years ago, would this be the longest chapter?)

2. In our times, marriage is presented as simply one of many "lifestyle choices." Yet the text states that there are only a few, and very elevated at that, reasons for freely renouncing marriage. What are they?

   a.

   b.

3. Consider this example: A young man in his mid-twenties has graduated from college and secured a good paying job with tremendous opportunities for advancement. He openly tells anyone who will listen that he has no intention of getting married so that he can have a nicer house and buy a new car whenever he wants. Furthermore, a family might weigh him down as he strives to advance in his job. What precisely is sinful about this man's outlook on life? Is his refusal to marry, in and of itself, sinful?

I. MAN AND WOMAN CREATED IN A STATE OF MARRIAGE

4. When did Adam and Eve get married?

A. THE FIRST CREATION STORY

5. How does God create men and women in the First Creation Story?

B. THE SECOND CREATION STORY

6. How does God create men and women in the Second Creation Story?

II. THE PROCREATION OF HUMAN LIFE IN THE FAMILY

7. Even without a Bible, we would know by the Natural Law that the procreation of children should take place only within marriage. What empirical evidence does the text cite as proof of this?

8. The text clearly states:"Every person has the right to be born of a *known* man and a *known* woman, whom he can call father and mother, and to carry out his normal existence in a home" (emphasis added). List some practices which are becoming more and more accepted in our society, that this statement would exclude.

III. THE PURPOSES OF MARRIAGE

A. GOOD OF THE SPOUSES

9. As we saw earlier in this study (review Question #15 in Chapter 11 of this workbook), one of the questions asked of a couple immediately before they receive the Sacrament of Matrimony is, "Have you come here freely and without reservation to give yourselves to each other in marriage?" How is this question directly related to the good of the spouses?

B. PROCREATION

10. In biblical times, children, and especially large families, were seen as a sign of God's favor and blessing. How are children and large families seen in our day and age?

11. The text states:"Children are always a source of joy when they are born out of the parents' love for one another."Given your answer in Question #10, why, according to this statement, are children perceived by our society in the way you described?

IV. JOYS OF MARRIAGE

12. Many people have the impression that religion, and especially the Catholic religion, teaches that genital sexual intimacy is "dirty" and sinful. What does the Catholic Church teach about the nature of these acts?

V. PROPERTIES OF MARRIAGE

A. EXCLUSIVITY

13. What is *polygamy*?

14. What is *polyandry*?

15. Polygamy has been a part of many societies throughout the centuries. As societies develop, what usually indicates the end of the acceptance of polygamy within a society?

B. INDISSOLUBILITY

16. Name the two arguments that testify to the indissolubility of marriage.

   a.

   b.

17. The text speaks of a *ratified* and *consummated* marriage. These words are not defined in your text. Find out what they mean in regards to marriage.

    Ratified:

    Consummated:

18. What is the only force that can dissolve a ratified and consummated marriage between a baptized man and a baptized woman?

19. Why does the Catholic Church not grant divorces?

20. Why does the Catholic Church not recognize divorce (i.e., divorces granted by civil courts)?

21. St. Paul writes in 1 Corinthians 7: 12-15:

    "¹²To the rest I say, not the Lord, that if any brother has a wife who is an unbeliever, and she consents to live with him, he should not divorce her. ¹³If any woman has a husband who is an unbeliever, and he consents to live with her, she should not divorce him. ¹⁴For the unbelieving husband is consecrated through his wife, and the unbelieving wife is consecrated through her husband. Otherwise, your children would be unclean, but as it is, they are holy. ¹⁵But if the unbelieving partner desires to separate, let it be so; in such a case the brother or sister is not bound. For God has called us to peace."

    To St. Paul, and to the Church today, "unbelieving" means an unbaptized person who has nothing to do with the Christian faith. In such a case, when is St. Paul allowing for a marriage to be dissolved?

22. Explain the *Petrine Privilege* (also called the Privilege of the Faith).

23. What does it mean for a marriage to be non-consummated, and when might this happen?

VI. ANNULMENT

24. After an extensive investigation, both civil and Church authorities will grant annulments for marriages if the evidence warrants. What is an annulment?

25. What would be the grounds for a judge to grant a civil annulment for a failed civil marriage?

26. What would be the grounds for the Church granting an annulment for a failed sacramental marriage? (For a clue, look back again to Question #15 in Chapter 11 of this workbook, and review the criteria of the Church for a valid sacramental marriage.)

27. In order to attempt marriage again in the Catholic Church, an annulment is necessary. In the civil courts, however, there is no such requirement. Why would someone petition an annulment from a civil court if it is not needed for either another civil marriage or a Sacramental marriage?

28. What is the difference between an annulment and a divorce?

VII. THE DIFFERENT DIMENSIONS OF HUMAN SEXUALITY

A. HUMAN AFFECTION

29. Many young people have been subjected to misdirected and misinformed discussions on sexuality. When being taught about contraception by the public school system, agencies like Planned Parenthood, and even, sadly, their parents, they are told something to the effect of: "If you can't control yourself, you need to protect yourself." What does the text say about the human capacity to control sexual appetites?

30. How is a married couple "making love" to each other different from two people "having sex?"

B. PHYSICAL MANIFESTATION

31. How is the physical manifestation of human sexuality a principal reason why two people of the same sex cannot "marry?"

C. PLEASURE

32. Sexual pleasure is clearly one of the benefits and joys of the married life that draws the spouses closer together. Under what kind of circumstances can this same pleasure drive spouses apart?

D. PROCREATION

33. It is by God's design that affection, the complementariness of male and female genitalia, the physical pleasure of sexual acts, and procreation all come together in the natural and human use of sex. This means that if any of these are missing, the natural and human dimension of sexuality is removed, and what is left is inhuman, unnatural, and basically sinful. Give two examples of how this is so.

VIII. CATHOLIC DOCTRINE REGARDING SEXUALITY

34. What does Catholic doctrine take into account in regard to human sexuality?

A. POSITIVE VALUE OF SEXUALITY

35. Catholic teaching places a high value on human sexuality. How has contemporary Western society (i.e., Western Europe and the United States) greatly devalued human sexuality?

B. HUMAN CONTROL OF SEXUALITY

36. Back in Question #26, we examined the sinful and erroneous teaching given by certain agencies and even some parents to young people that, "If you can't control yourself, you need to protect yourself." The Church teaches that since we are made in God's image and likeness, we have a mind, will, and intellect that is similar to God's. This being the case, we should all be capable of controlling ourselves, including our sexual appetites and desires. Assume that by reading this textbook and by participating in this class you and all of your classmates are convinced that indeed you can control your behavior, and as a result of this, all of you remain chaste until marriage. What material gain will the textbook company or your teacher (or your parents, the Church, your pastor, youth minister, etc) get if you buy into this way of thinking?

37. Now, assume your classroom is visited by a representative of Planned Parenthood who comes to "educate you about your reproductive choices." After a lengthy presentation on the various types of birth control that are available to you, *without your parents' consent or even being informed*, the Planned Parenthood "educator" tells the group, "Look, in an ideal world, we would all wait until we are in a committed relationship* before having sex. But this isn't an ideal world, so if you can't control yourself, you at least need to protect yourself." If you and your classmates buy into this way of thinking, what does Planned Parenthood get?

  * It is interesting to note that when such agencies speak of relationships, the word "marriage" is always avoided.

38. With the answers to Questions #33 and #34 in mind, who do you think has your best interests at heart?

C. UPRIGHT USE OF SEXUALITY

39. The text lists a number of sexual acts that are gravely sinful outside of marriage. Write the word from the vocabulary list that is synonymous with each term.

    a. Extra-marital sex: _____

    b. Pre-marital sex: _____

    c. Solitary sexual acts: _____

40. Bob is a married man who engages is an extra-marital affair with Sue who is a single woman. By having this sexual encounter, Bob commits the mortal sin of _____, while Sue commits the equally grave sin of _____.

41. What are the weapons a Catholic has to protect him/herself from falling into these sins?

IX. CHASTITY AS A VIRTUE: PURITY OF BODY AND HEART

42. What is the definition of *chastity*?

43. What is the difference between *chastity* and *continence*?

44. How would a high school aged boyfriend and girlfriend be showing genuine love for one another by encouraging one another to be chaste, in spite of their many temptations?

45. Look at the diagram.

    What happens to the boy and the girl as they become closer to God?

46. On the other hand, what if the boy, while dating the girl, is looking at pornography on the internet, engaging in sexually vulgar conversations with his buddies in the locker room, and masturbating regularly? The diagram would look like this.

    As such sinful behavior clearly moves the boy away from God, what *will* happen between him and his girlfriend?

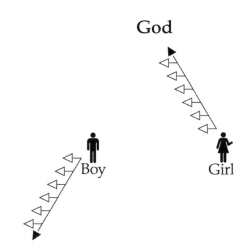

47. What if the boy and the girl are engaging in sinful behavior such as getting drunk at parties, engaging in heavy petting, oral sex, and finally sexual intercourse (all outside of marriage)? The diagram would look like this.

    As the boy and girl are both separating themselves more and more from God, what happens to their relationship as a couple?

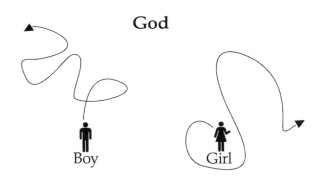

X. SINS AGAINST CHASTITY: OLD TESTAMENT TEACHINGS

48. Review the sins against chastity on page 267 of the text. Are these things evil because God has forbidden them, or has God forbidden them because they are evil?

XI. SINS AGAINST CHASTITY: NEW TESTAMENT TEACHINGS

49. What additional "twist" does Jesus put on sins against chastity in Matthew 5: 28?

XII. SINS AGAINST CHASTITY: DOCTRINE OF SACRED TRADITION

50. Read the piece of the letter from St. Justin Martyr to the Emperor Antoninus Pius that is reproduced on page 269 of the text. What kind of life had the pagan converts to Christianity been living before becoming Christians?

51. Yet these people converted to Christianity, and left this way of life behind. As long as they remained pagans, they could continue on in the dissolute lifestyle that much of American society idolizes and aspires to. Why would they voluntarily leave it and take on the disciplines of the Christian life?

XIII. SINS AGAINST CHASTITY: THE TEACHING OF THE MAGISTERIUM

52. The list of sins against chastity as taught by the Magisterium of the Church is on page 269, and is quite complete. A question we might ask ourselves: The Church is routinely ridiculed in universities, in movies and television, and by activists in the gay movement, women's movement, and many others for these teachings. In our world that is held hostage by terrorism, we find that a small number of crazy people can convince young people to blow themselves up, murdering as many others as possible in the process, by indoctrinating these young people with lies about the teachings of Islam. How is it that these fanatics can convince their young people to blow themselves up by telling them lies, while parents, pastors, and even the pope cannot convince people to lead lives of chastity by telling them the truth?

XIV. CHASTITY IN MARRIAGE: RESPONSIBLE PARENTHOOD AND NATURAL FAMILY PLANNING

53. Under what conditions does Catholic teaching allow for the use of artificial contraceptives?

54. Explain in simple terms how Natural Family Planning works, both to help achieve pregnancy and to avoid it.

55. The ideal is for couples to remain open to receiving the children that God sends them. They agree to this on during their wedding. If they do decide to avail themselves to Natural Family Planning (as the only morally licit means of birth control), what conditions must be met?

    a.

    b.

    c.

    d.

    e.

XV. CONTRACEPTION AND THE DESTRUCTION OF MARRIAGE

56. Over the past century or so, the rate of divorce in the United States has been steadily climbing. Graphically, the trend looks something like this.

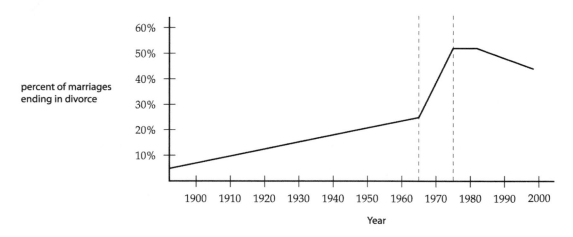

Note that in the period from about 1965 to 1975, the divorce rate *doubled* from about 25% to around 52% of marriages ending in divorce. Why do you think there was such a steep increase in the divorce rate during this period of time?

57. Since about the 1990's we see the divorce rate dropping a little. Why do you think this is, and can you think of a connection to artificial contraception that might explain it?

58. Many so-called "contraceptives" are not, as their name indicates, "actions against conception." Instead, what are they?

59. In his encyclical letter *Humanæ vitæ*, Pope Paul VI made the following predictions about what would happen if artificial contraceptives were to unleashed upon the world. Name an example of how each of his predictions have come true (the numbers are not part of the Pope's original text. They have been added to help you answer the question).

§17 "Upright men can even better convince themselves of the solid grounds on which the teaching of the Church in this field is based, if they care to reflect upon the consequences of methods of artificial birth control. (a) Let them consider, first of all, how wide and easy a road would this be opened up towards conjugal infidelity and (b) the general lowering of morality. (c) Not much experience is needed in order to know human weakness, and to understand that [people]—especially the young who are so vulnerable at this point—have need of encouragement to be faithful to the moral law, so that they must not be offered some easy means of eluding its observance. (d) It is also to be feared that the man, growing used to anti-conceptive practices, may finally lose respect for the woman and, no longer caring for her physical and psychological equilibrium, may come to the point of considering her as a mere instrument of selfish enjoyment, and no longer as his respected and beloved companion.

(e) Let it be considered also that a dangerous weapon would thus be placed in the hands of those public authorities who take no heed of moral exigencies ... Who will stop rulers from favoring, and even imposing upon their peoples, if they were to consider it necessary, the method of contraception which they judge to be most efficacious?

    a.

    b.

    c.

    d.

    e.

XVI. ASSISTED FERTILIZATION AND ARTIFICIAL INSEMINATION

60. What is another term for "assisted fertilization?"

61. Why is revelation (i.e., the Bible) silent on such issues as assisted fertilization?

62. Since the Bible offers no guidance on these issues, who is the competent authority to help us make correct moral judgments about such actions?

A. ASSISTED FERTILIZATION

63. When are techniques using assisted fertilization morally allowable?

B. HOMOLOGOUS ARTIFICIAL INSEMINATION

64. What is homologous artificial insemination?

65. List the two ways that homologous artificial insemination is done and explain each.

    a. _____ is when . . .

    b. _____ is when . . .

66. Why is the homologous artificial insemination technique you described in Question #65-a immoral?

67. Why is the homologous artificial insemination technique you described in Question #65-b immoral?

C. HETEROLOGOUS ARTIFICIAL INSEMINATION

68. What is heterologous artificial insemination?

69. Why is this immoral?

XVII. "YOU SHALL NOT COVET YOUR NEIGHBOR'S WIFE."

70. What does it mean to "covet?"

71. Why is coveting the spouse of another sinful? As long as there is no adultery, where is the harm?

MARK AND MADDIE RESPOND

Dear (Name withheld) —

We cannot help but to notice the hostile tone of your letter, but we do appreciate you writing and will try to answer your questions. The main reason why people your age are always "being lectured to all the time about sex," as you put it, is because we live in a time where sexual promiscuity is out of control. The sinfulness of this is bad enough. But the human misery and suffering that results from it only exacerbates the problem. Over the past few decades, as artificial contraceptives have opened wide the door to adultery and fornication, we have seen dramatic increases in children born out of wedlock (and thus into poverty), acts of violence against women, and divorces. Yes, sex is natural and beautiful and the Church does teach this, but only within marriage. It's kind of like food. Rich foods are certainly tasty, but if that is all that someone eats, there will certainly be health problems. We must also eat for health. Sexual pleasure is certainly desirable, but only under the circumstances prescribed by God. To use sex outside of God's wise plan only invites grief and pain. We really hope you give your opinions about sexuality some serious thought and prayer. As it stands, you are setting yourself up for a life of disappointment and pain. We will keep you in our prayers.

Mark & Maddie

Name _____

Date _____

Hour _____

Chapter 16: The Seventh and Tenth Commandments:
YOU SHALL NOT STEAL.
YOU SHALL NOT COVET YOUR NEIGHBOR'S GOODS.

Dear Mark and Maddie —

What's the deal with everyone always complaining about how much they don't have, how much everyone else has, and how somebody is always oppressing someone else to get what they have??! I don't get it. I work a part time job, and both of my parents work. We don't live like kings, but we are not poor either. I volunteer with our church youth group at a food pantry for the poor, so I have seen how some people are scraping to get by. But I also know that a lot of people are poor because of bad decisions they have made. If that's the case, why should I be made to feel bad for making good decisions?

— Kyle

INTRODUCTION

1. What does Church teaching demand of economic systems?

2. In Catholic teaching, which units of society have top priority?

3. The text states, "Individual and private initiatives should be encouraged as the best way of producing wealth." Which economic system is this describing?

4. According to Church teaching, how should individual needs be met and duties be fulfilled?

I. BIBLICAL DOCTRINE CONCERNING
HUMAN RELATIONS TO MATERIAL THINGS

5. For whom did God create the earth?

II. UNIVERSAL DESTINY OF CREATED GOODS

6. What is meant by the term "universal destiny of goods?"

III. THE RIGHT TO PROPERTY

7. Upon what does the Church base its claim that people have a right to private property?

IV. THE UNIVERSAL DESTINY OF GOODS
AND THE RIGHT TO PRIVATE PROPERTY

8. So far, we have seen that the Church insists on the individual's right to private property, while also demanding that all of creation is intended by God for the good of all his children. These two ideas may seem to contradict each other. Write the name of the concept that unites them and explain it.

9. The last words of the Fifth Amendment to the Constitution of the United States reads:

    ". . . nor shall private property be taken for public use, without just compensation."

    Which social principle does this illustrate?

V. THE SOCIAL DOCTRINE OF THE CHURCH

10. What historical event caused the Church to develop her social doctrine?

11. Over the past two centuries, various popes have written on social issues such as workers' rights, the economy, etc. The first was an encyclical called _____ that was written by Leo XIII, and released on May 15, 1891. On the topic of social doctrine, the encyclical called _____, written by _____ , was released May 1, 1991.

12. List five areas that the social doctrine of the Church covers.

    a.

    b.

    c.

    d.

    e.

13. Why, according to Church teachings, does God want everyone participating in the goods of creation?

14. Give a concrete example of your answer in Question #13.

VI. THE DUTY OF CHRISTIANS TO PARTICIPATE IN PUBLIC LIFE

15. In general, how is the Christian to influence public life?

VII. INTERNATIONAL SOLIDARITY

16. When, according to *The Catechism of the Catholic Church,* are richer nations most obligated to share their excess wealth with poorer nations?

VIII. RESPECT FOR NATURE: ECOLOGY

17. From its Greek roots, what does the word "ecology" mean?

18. How do some ecological activists go too far in their desire to protect the earth?

19. How do some individuals go too far in their desire for the goods of the earth?

IX. "DO NOT STEAL": RESPECT FOR PRIVATE PROPERTY

20. What precisely is theft?

21. Other than the outright taking of someone else's property, what are some other examples of theft?

22. What is robbery?

X. "YOU SHALL NOT COVET."

23. What does it mean to covet (as in goods)?

24. What is greed?

25. What is avarice?

XI. RESTITUTION

26. Is direct restitution always possible? Give examples.

MARK AND MADDIE RESPOND

Dear Kyle —

You bring up some good points in your letter. Much of poverty is indeed caused by bad decisions, such as dropping out of high school and having children out of wed-lock. These are, without a doubt, causes of poverty that are totally avoidable. And it is good to see that you and your family work hard. Where we think you might be confused is in thinking that once you earn something it is yours to do with as you please. But, Kyle, nothing we have is ours forever. We are stewards of what God has loaned to us, not absolute owners. When we die, we take nothing out of this world with us. For this reason, once we have seen to our needs and the needs of our family, we need to be mindful of the needs of the poor. We think you are right in that it seems that in our day and age, there is almost total emphasis on the perceived claims that the poor have upon the rich, without a corresponding emphasis on a requirement that the poor avoid those behaviors which we know cause poverty. But in the end, in the eyes of God, we are all poor. Try to spend more time being thankful to God for giving you and your family productive work to do. Keep working at the food pantry, try to see Jesus in the faces of the poor, and see if that doesn't change your outlook.

In Christ's peace,

Mark & Maddie

Chapter 17: The Eighth Commandment:
YOU SHALL NOT BEAR FALSE WITNESS
AGAINST YOUR NEIGHBOR.

Dear Mark and Maddie —

I went to a party that my parents told me that I could not go to. When they asked me if I had gone, I lied (okay, I admit it) and said that I was at one of my friend's house. What they didn't tell me was that they had checked up on me before they asked me. They know who my best friend is, and called his house before my dad went out looking for me. He saw my car parked outside of the house where the party was. My parents took my car away from me and won't say when I'll get it back. I just think I'm getting a raw deal. Yeah, there was some bad stuff going on at the party, but not everyone was involved, and certainly not me. Also, my parents are all mad because I lied to them, but didn't they lie to me, setting me up the way they did? And besides, everybody lies. After the arguments and yelling died down, my dad tried to talk to me. He said that even though he's not proud of it he even tells lies sometimes. So what's the big deal? I told a lie, but nobody got hurt. Why can't we just accept the fact that it's not a perfect world and people don't always tell the truth?

— Neil

INTRODUCTION

1. Western culture is typically understood to include Western Europe and North America, particularly the United States. We did not develop in a vacuum. From which two ancient civilizations did our philosophy (i.e., our desire to know what things are) come from?

    a.

    b.

2. The rational knowledge upon which our civilization is built, is based on what two things?

    a.

    b.

I. TRUTH IN THE OLD TESTAMENT

3. The consistent theme in the better part of this section is that the Ten Commandments are a minimal moral and ethical code. Based on what we have seen so far in this study, if the Decalogue describes the minimum in the most generic of terms, where do we find the fullness of Christian life?

4. Perhaps it would help to have a map. Look at the graphic below, and mark where you think you are on the continuum.

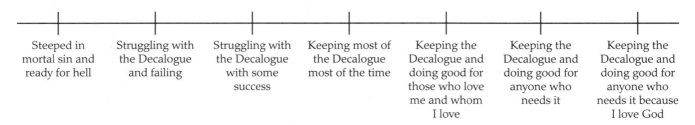

| Steeped in mortal sin and ready for hell | Struggling with the Decalogue and failing | Struggling with the Decalogue with some success | Keeping most of the Decalogue most of the time | Keeping the Decalogue and doing good for those who love me and whom I love | Keeping the Decalogue and doing good for anyone who needs it | Keeping the Decalogue and doing good for anyone who needs it because I love God |

5. Now that you have an idea as to where you stand, what do you need to move closer to the ideal?

6. According to the Law of Moses, in the event of an accusation made against someone, the word of two witnesses was all that was necessary to convict a person of the crime in question (See Deuteronomy 17: 6-7 and 19: 15-21). Why would the Eighth Commandment have been so important to ancient Israel?

7. Our legal system is much more complex. Yet why is the Eighth Commandment still just as important to us?

II. TRUTH IN THE NEW TESTAMENT

8. What distinguishes human beings from animals?

9. Because of our distinction from animals, what four activities define our natural vocation in regards to the truth?

    a.

    b.

    c.

    d.

10. As with the rest of the Ten Commandments, the Eighth Commandment is further enriched by . . .

    a.

    b.

    c.

III. TRUTH AND FREEDOM: "THE TRUTH WILL SET YOU FREE."

11. Imagine that a young man wants to compete in triathlons. Yet he insists that he can prepare for miles of running, bicycling, and swimming by sitting around playing computer games and eating junk food. It may seem silly to try to explain it, but why will this not work? Is there some old fashioned authority figure holding some outdated doctrines over our aspiring athlete's head refusing to allow him to compete in the sport of his choosing?

12. We have visited this topic a number of times during the course of this study. The text states: "... the way to reach true freedom is through knowledge of the truth. Ignorance, error, mistakes, or falsehoods inhibit human freedom." Yet how many people consistently act as if freedom means the license to do as they please. Explain how this perversion of the idea of freedom ends up imprisoning people (use an example or two).

IV. SPREADING TRUTH

13. What has been your experience with the news media? Do find that you can believe what you read in the newspaper or see on television?

14. What is the attitude of the Magisterium concerning the media?

V. TO TELL THE TRUTH: HONESTY VERSUS DISHONESTY

15. What precisely is a lie?

16. Does everyone always have a right to hear the truth? Give an example to back up your answer.

A. A LIE CAUSES DAMAGE TO THE ONE WHO TELLS IT.

17. How does a lie cause damage to the one who tells it? Give an example to back up your answer.

B. IT PRODUCES VICE IN HUMAN RELATIONS.

18. How does a lie produce vice in human relations? Give an example to back up your answer.

C. IT DAMAGES SOCIETY.

19. How do lies damage society? Give an example to back up your answer.

VI. GRAVITY OF A LIE

A. THE MATERIAL RELATED TO THE LIE
B. THE INTENTION
C. THE CIRCUMSTANCES THAT MOTIVATE THE LIE
D. THE EFFECTS OF A LIE

20. Use the criteria for the gravity of a lie to determine how serious a lie would be under the following circumstances.

    a. Frances comes home from the store with a bag containing her mother's birthday present. Her mother sees her come in the front door and asks her what is in the bag, to which Frances responds, "Oh nothing, just some shampoo and deodorant I picked up at the store."

       • Is the material related to the lie serious?

(continued next page)

- Is there the intention to cause harm?

- Are the circumstances motivating the lie causing serious evil?

- Is the lie causing evil effects?

In general, how do you judge this lie?

b. What about Neil's lie in his letter to Mark and Maddie?

- Is the material related to the lie serious?

- Is there the intention to cause harm?

- Are the circumstances motivating the lie causing serious evil?

- Is the lie causing evil effects?

In general, how do you judge this lie?

c. Four students vandalize the school building causing some expensive damage. Sadly, the administration has blamed the wrong person. The four guilty students stand by and say nothing. And, in fact, among themselves, they laugh about the fact that the other student is taking all the blame.

- Is the material related to the lie serious?

- Is there the intention to cause harm?

- Are the circumstances motivating the lie causing serious evil?

• Is the lie causing evil effects?

In general, how do you judge this lie?

VII. SINS AGAINST ANOTHER'S REPUTATION

A. CALUMNY

21. What is *calumny*?

B. DETRACTION

22. What is *detraction*?

C. RASH JUDGMENT

23. What is *rash judgment*?

24. Write the name of the sin against another's reputation next to the situation that best describes it.

_____ Out of fear and desperation, a young man confides in his best friend that he is homosexual, begging his friend to keep it between them. The "friend" then spreads the news around the whole school.

_____ There is a new kid at school who seems kind of strange. One afternoon, you see him pulled over in his car by a police officer. You assume he is guilty of some serious crime involving illegal drugs. In fact, the officer pulled him over because his turning signal light was not working.

_____ A very popular and handsome boy has just broken up with his girlfriend, and begins to date another girl. The ex-girlfriend proceeds to invent stories about the boy which she spreads around, hoping to cause them to break up.

VIII. THE DUTY TO MAKE REPARATION

25. What is the fundamental problem or difficulty with trying to make reparations after committing a sin of calumny?

IX. SECRETS

26. Which are the most seriously binding secrets?

27. When may a priest tell what he has heard in confession?

28. Steve is put jail in after a court finds him guilty of embezzling money from his employer. He goes to confession to Fr. John, and confesses his sin of theft and his desire to pay the money back once he is out of jail. Fr. John has known through reading the paper and conversations with Steve's wife what has been going on. Sometime later, Bill comments to Fr. John, "Didn't Steve go to jail for stealing all that money from where he worked?" And Fr. John says, "Yes, he did." Did Fr. John break the seal of confession? Why or why not?

MARK AND MADDIE RESPOND

Dear Neil —

You did not mention your age, but we assume you are a minor. In such a case, your parents are responsible for you, and have the right to check-up on your doings and your whereabouts. We think it was a good thing they did for you—they gave you the chance to come clean. Imagine how much you would have shot up in their estimation if you had told them that you went to the party. They would have been disappointed that you disobeyed them, and you still may have been punished, but imagine what that would have done to your reputation, and not to mention to your character. You are doing some dangerous thinking, Neil. You say that since your dad and everyone else lies, what's the big deal? Well, it is a big deal! Think about it. If you are going to use your dad's faults and shortcomings as your standard of behavior, then the best you will ever be able to do is the worst that he has done. Is that what you want? You're right, we don't live in a perfect world, but it is up to all of us to try to make it better. Following the Ten Commandments is a good way to start. All we can say is work on getting your parents' trust back, and tell the truth. You will be amazed at how easy your life will get.

Mark & Maddie

Catholic Prayers and Devotions

In any endeavor, there are certain basics that must be learned, memorized, and internalized.
These prayers and devotions are fundamental to the life of an active, practicing Catholic.

The Ten Commandments

1. I am the LORD your God: You shall not have strange gods before me.
2. You shall not take the name of the LORD your God in vain.
3. Remember to keep holy the LORD's day.
4. Honor your father and your mother.
5. You shall not kill.
6. You shall not commit adultery.
7. You shall not steal.
8. You shall not bear false witness against your neighbor.
9. You shall not covet your neighbor's wife.
10. You shall not covet your neighbor's goods.

The Precepts of the Church   *[See CCC #2042-2043, Second Edition, 1997]*

1. You shall attend Mass on Sundays and holy days of obligation and rest from servile labor.
2. You shall confess your sins at least once a year.
3. You shall receive the Sacrament of the Eucharist at least during the Easter season.
4. You shall observe the days of fasting and abstinence established by the Church.
5. You shall help provide for the needs of the Church.

The Corporal Works of Mercy

- Feeding the hungry
- Giving drink to the thirsty
- Clothing the naked
- Sheltering the homeless
- Visiting the sick
- Visiting the imprisoned
- Burying the dead

The Spiritual Works of Mercy

- Counseling the doubtful
- Instructing the ignorant
- Admonishing sinners
- Comforting the afflicted
- Forgiving offenses
- Bearing wrongs patiently
- Praying for the living and the dead

The Gifts of the Holy Spirit

- Wisdom
- Understanding
- Counsel
- Fortitude
- Knowledge
- Piety
- Fear of the Lord

Theological Virtues

- Faith
- Hope
- Charity

The Sins that Cry to Heaven

- The murder of the innocent (cf. Genesis 4: 10)
- Homosexual behavior (cf. Genesis 18: 20, 19: 13)
- The enslavement of people (cf. Exodus 3: 7-10)
- Oppression of the widow, orphan, or alien (cf. Exodus 22: 21-24)
- Withholding wages from the laborer (cf. Deuteronomy 24: 14-15)

"The catechetical tradition recalls that there are *'sins that cry to heaven'*: the blood of Abel; the sin of the Sodomites; ignoring the cry of the people oppressed in Egypt and that of the foreigner, the widow, and the orphan; injustice to the wage earner" (*The Catechism* 1867).

Capital Sins

- Pride
- Covetousness
- Lust
- Anger
- Gluttony
- Envy
- Sloth

Opposed Virtues

- Humility
- Liberality
- Chastity
- Meekness
- Temperance
- Brotherly love
- Diligence

Cardinal Virtues

- Prudence
- Justice
- Fortitude
- Temperance

The Beatitudes   (Matthew 5: 3-12)

- Blessed are the poor in spirit, for theirs is the kingdom of heaven.
- Blessed are those who mourn, for they shall be comforted.
- Blessed are the meek, for they shall inherit the earth.
- Blessed are those who hunger and thirst for righteousness, for they shall be satisfied.
- Blessed are the merciful, for they shall obtain mercy.
- Blessed are the pure of heart, for they shall see God.
- Blessed are the peacemakers, for they shall be called the sons of God.
- Blessed are those who are persecuted for righteousness' sake, for theirs is the kingdom of heaven.
- Blessed are you when men revile you and persecute you and utter all kinds of evil against you falsely on my account. Rejoice and be glad, for your reward is great in heaven.

The Sign of the Cross

In the name of the Father, and of the Son, and of the Holy Spirit. Amen

The Lord's Prayer

Our Father, who art in heaven, hallowed be thy name. Thy kingdom come; thy will be done on earth as it is in heaven. Give us this day our daily bread; and forgive us our trespasses as we forgive those who trespass against us; and lead us not into temptation, but deliver us from evil. Amen.

The Hail Mary

Hail, Mary, full of grace, the Lord is with thee; blessed art thou among women, and blessed is the fruit of thy womb, Jesus. Holy Mary, Mother of God, pray for us sinners, now and at the hour of our death. Amen.

The Glory Be (The Doxology)

Glory be to the Father, and to the Son, and to the Holy Spirit. As it was in the beginning, is now, and ever shall be, world without end. Amen.

Morning Offering

O Jesus, through the Immaculate Heart of Mary, I offer you my prayers, works, joys, and sufferings of this day for all the intentions of your Sacred Heart, in union with the holy sacrifice of the Mass throughout the world, in thanksgiving for your favors, in reparation for my sins, for the intentions of all my relatives and friends, and in particular for the intentions of the Holy Father. Amen.

Consecration to the Blessed Virgin Mary

My Queen and my Mother, I give myself entirely to you, and, in proof of my affection, I give you my eyes, my ears, my tongue, my heart, my whole being without reserve. Since I am your own, keep me and guard me as your property and possession. Amen.

Act of Faith

O my God, I firmly believe that you are one God in three divine Persons, Father, Son, and Holy Spirit; I believe that your divine Son became man and died for our sins, and that he shall come to judge the living and the dead. I believe these and all the truths that the holy Catholic Church teaches, because you have revealed them, who can neither deceive nor be deceived.

Act of Hope

O my God, relying on your almighty power and infinite mercy and promises, I hope to obtain pardon for my sins, the help of your grace, and life everlasting, through the merits of Jesus Christ, my Lord and Redeemer.

Act of Charity

O my God, I love you above all things, with my whole heart and soul, because you are all-good and worthy of all love. I love my neighbor as myself for the love of You. I forgive all who have injured me and ask pardon of all whom I have injured.

Prayer to One's Guardian Angel

Angel of God, my guardian dear, to whom God's love commits me here, ever this day (night) be at my side, to light and guard, to rule and guide. Amen.

The *Angelus* (*Said outside the Easter Season*)

V. The Angel of the Lord declared unto Mary;

R. And she conceived by the Holy Spirit.
Hail Mary . . .

V. Behold the handmaid of the Lord.

R. Be it done unto me according to your word.
Hail Mary . . .

V. And the Word was made flesh,

R. And dwelt among us.
Hail Mary . . .

V. Pray for us, O holy Mother of God.

R. That we may be made worthy of the promises of Christ.

V. Let us pray.
Pour forth we beseech you, O Lord, your grace into our hearts, that we, to whom the incarnation of Christ, your Son, was made known by the message of an angel, may by his passion and cross be brought to the glory of his resurrection, through the same Christ our Lord.

R. Amen.

Regina cæli (*Said during the Easter Season*)

V. Queen of Heaven, rejoice! Alleluia.

R. For he whom you did merit to bear. Alleluia.

V. Has risen, as he said. Alleluia.

R. Pray for us to God. Alleluia.

V. Rejoice and be glad, O Virgin Mary. Alleluia.

R. For the Lord is truly risen. Alleluia.

V. Let us pray.
O God who gave joy to the world through the resurrection of your Son, our Lord Jesus Christ, grant, we beseech you, that through the intercession of the Virgin Mary, his Mother, we may obtain the joys of everlasting life, through the same Christ our Lord.

R. Amen.

Prayer to the Holy Spirit

V. Come, O Holy Spirit, fill the hearts of your faithful and enkindle in them the fire of your love. Send forth your Spirit, and they shall be created.

R. And you shall renew the face of the earth.

V. Let us pray.
O God, who has taught the hearts of the faithful by the light of the Holy Spirit, grant that by the gift of the same Spirit we may be always truly wise and ever rejoice in his consolation. Through Christ our Lord.

R. Amen

Eternal Rest

V. Eternal rest grant unto them (him/her), O Lord,

R. And let perpetual light shine upon them (him/her).

V. May they (he/she) rest in peace.

R. Amen.

V. May their (his/her) soul(s) and the souls of all the faithful departed, through the mercy of God, rest in peace.

R. Amen.

Blessing Before A Meal

Bless us, O Lord, and these your gifts, which we are about to receive from your bounty, through Christ our Lord. Amen.

Thanksgiving After A Meal

We give you thanks, almighty God, for all your benefits, who live and reign forever and ever. Amen.

The Apostles' Creed

I believe in God, the Father almighty, creator of heaven and earth. I believe in Jesus Christ, his only Son, our Lord. He was conceived by the power of the Holy Spirit and born of the Virgin Mary. He suffered under Pontius Pilate, was crucified, died, and was buried. He descended into hell. On the third day he rose again. He ascended into heaven, and is seated at the right hand of the Father. He will come again to judge the living and the dead. I believe in the Holy Spirit, the holy Catholic Church, the communion of saints, the forgiveness of sins, the resurrection of the body, and life everlasting. Amen.

Fatima Prayer

O my Jesus, forgive us our sins, save us from the fire of hell, draw all souls to heaven, especially those who are in most need of your mercy. Amen.

Hail Holy Queen

Hail, holy Queen, Mother of mercy, our life, our sweetness, and our hope. To you do we cry, poor banished children of Eve. To you do we send up our sighs, mourning and weeping in this valley of tears. Turn then, most gracious advocate, thine eyes of mercy towards us, and after this exile show unto us the blessed fruit of your womb, Jesus. O clement, O loving, O sweet virgin Mary.

V. Pray for us, O holy Mother of God.

R. That we may be made worthy of the promises of Christ.

Rosary Prayer

O God, whose only-begotten Son, by his life, death, and resurrection, has purchased for us the rewards of eternal life; grant, we beseech you, that, we, who meditate on these mysteries of the most holy Rosary of the Blessed Virgin Mary, may imitate what they contain, and obtain what they promise. Through Christ our Lord. Amen.

The *Memorare*

Remember, O most gracious Virgin Mary, that never was it known that anyone who fled to your protection, implored your help, or sought your intercession was left unaided. Inspired with this confidence, I fly unto you, O Virgin of virgins, my Mother. To you I come, before you I stand, sinful and sorrowful. O Mother of the Word incarnate, despise not my petitions, but in your mercy hear and answer me. Amen.

Act of Contrition .

O my God, I am heartily sorry for having offended you, and I detest all my sins, because I dread the loss of heaven and the pains of hell; but most of all because they offend you, my God, who are all good and deserving of all of my love. I firmly resolve, with the help of your grace, to confess my sins, to do penance, and to amend my life. Amen.

Prayer to St. Michael

Saint Michael the Archangel, defend us in battle; be our defense against the wickedness and snares of the devil. May God rebuke him, we humbly pray. And do you, O prince of the heavenly host, by the power of God thrust into hell Satan and all the evil spirits who prowl about the world for the ruin of souls. Amen.

How to Pray the Rosary

1. Holding the Crucifix in your hand, make the Sign of the Cross and pray the Apostles' Creed.
2. On the first bead after the Crucifix, pray the Our Father.
3. Pray one Hail Mary on each of the next three beads, asking God to increase faith, hope, and charity in your life.
4. On the bead after these three, pray the Glory Be, announce the First Mystery, and pray the Our Father.
5. Pray one Hail Mary for each of the ten following beads, and end them by praying the Glory Be and the Fatima Prayer.
6. Announce the Second Mystery and repeat steps four and five. Do the same for the Third, Fourth, and Fifth Mysteries.
7. After the Fatima Prayer for the Fifth Mystery, pray the Hail Holy Queen, the Rosary Prayer, and end with the Sign of the cross.

The Mysteries of the Rosary

The Joyful Mysteries
1. The Annunciation
2. The Visitation
3. The Nativity
4. The Presentation
5. The Finding of Jesus in the Temple

The Luminous Mysteries
1. The Baptism of Christ in the Jordan
2. The Manifestation of Christ at the wedding of Cana
3. The Proclamation of the Kingdom of God, with his call to conversion
4. The Transfiguration
5. The Institution of the Eucharist

The Sorrowful Mysteries
1. The Agony in the Garden
2. The Scourging at the Pillar
3. The Crowning with Thorns
4. The Carrying of the Cross
5. The Crucifixion

The Glorious Mysteries
1. The Resurrection
2. The Ascension
3. The Descent of the Holy Spirit
4. The Assumption
5. The Coronation of the Blessed Virgin Mary